EASY STORIES IN ENGLISH FOR BEGINNERS

10 FAIRY TALES TO TAKE YOUR ENGLISH FROM OK TO GOOD AND FROM GOOD TO GREAT

ARIEL GOODBODY

D1292194

Cover design by Geoffrey Bunting

Print ISBN 978-1-914968-00-6

Some of these stories were originally released at
EasyStoriesInEnglish.com

CONTENTS

WHY YOU MUST READ

'Why do I need to read in English?'

My students often ask me this. They think, 'I go to classes, I do my homework, I watch films in English. Why should I read books?'

Actually, reading is the best way to improve your English. I will tell you why.

First, reading is very important now. In 2006, only 1 in 100 people went to university. Now, 7 in 100 people go to university[1]. All jobs need more reading and writing than 100 years ago[2]. This is true for everyone. It doesn't matter if you're an office worker or a mechanic.

Second, reading will improve your speaking, writing, vocabulary and grammar better than any other way. It won't improve your listening, but it will improve your vocabulary. And when you have a better vocabulary, you can listen more easily, and improve your listening that way.

In school, you probably read lots of English. You probably read boring textbooks and stories with exercises at the end.

But I'm not talking about that. I'm talking about reading for *pleasure*[3].

That means reading a book you enjoy because you enjoy it. You are not reading because your teacher said, 'Read this book.' You are not reading because you think, 'I should read this book.' You are reading because you want to.

In 1965, they did an experiment[4] in schools in America. These schools were for boys who had done crimes[5]. For example, some of them stole things. They gave some of the boys free books. They were fun books, like *James Bond*. They said, 'You can do what you want. You don't have to read the books.'

But the boys *did* read the books. They read a lot of books. Some boys read a book every two days.

After two years, they gave the students a test. The students who got the books got better at reading and writing, and they liked school more. The students who did not get the books did not get better at reading and writing. Actually, some of them got *worse*.

This isn't just true for native speakers[6]. They also did an experiment[7] on students learning English in the Fiji islands[8]. They used three ways to teach. The first way was normal English teaching. They did grammar classes, exercises and so on. The second way was reading in silence[9]. The students read books in class. The third way was reading together. The teacher read books to the students[10].

After one year, the two ways with reading were the best. They were much better than the students who did normal English classes. They did the experiment again in Singapore. There, the students who read in silence did very well. They did the best in grammar tests. Other students did grammar classes, but they did *worse* in grammar tests!

In normal classes, we try to remember grammar and vocabulary. When we read, we learn them naturally[11].

Maybe you're thinking, 'When I read in English, it's too hard! I have to use the dictionary all the time. It's boring. I can't do it.'

I understand. So I wrote this book. I think this book will make you like reading, because the stories are easy and fun. The early stories are short and easy, and the later stories are longer and harder. When you finish the book, you will think, 'Wow, I did it!'

I make a podcast[12] called *Easy Stories in English*. Nine of the stories in this book I wrote for *Easy Stories in English*. One of the stories I wrote for this book. But when I made this book, I made the stories better. Now you can read the stories at beginner, pre-intermediate, interme-diate or advanced levels. The stories are all fairy tales[13]. Some are very popular fairy tales, but some are not so popular. One of them I wrote myself.

Maybe you're thinking: 'Fairy tales? Fairy tales are for

children! I need *useful* vocabulary. I need to learn about business and science. That can't be fun!'

Actually, the vocabulary in these stories will be useful[14]. McQuillan[15] did an experiment where he looked at vocabulary in 22 novels[16]. 85% of the words were on academic word lists[17]. Rolls and Rogers[18] also did an experiment. They said, 'If students read a million words of science fiction[19], will they learn important science words for studying at university?' The answer was yes.

So yes, fairy tales are useful for you, too.

But I understand if you still don't believe me. When I learned about all this, I found it hard to believe, too. But I like to try new things, and I love learning languages.

So in 2017, I decided to do an experiment. I had wanted to learn Spanish for a long time, but I didn't learn much in normal classes. I said, 'I will read a million words in Spanish. Afterwards, I will see what my level is.' A million words is about twenty novels[20], so it was a lot of work.

I started with very easy reading, like this book. Then I started reading translations[21] of books that I knew in English. For example, I have read *Harry Potter* and *Game of Thrones* in English, so I read them in Spanish, too.

Finally, I read new books in Spanish. I read Latin American[22] authors[23] such as Isabel Allende, Luis Jorge Borges and Manuel Puig. I loved them. I also listened to podcasts[24], but I always read the transcripts and added the words to my goal.

After I finished reading a million words, I wrote and

talked to native speakers[25]. I was at an intermediate level. I could understand almost everything I read, I could understand people when they spoke clearly, and I could have conversations. And I had spent most my time reading, not speaking!

In one year I learned more than most students learn in five years.

I didn't try to remember grammar and vocabulary. I learned them naturally[26].

Maybe you're thinking, 'I don't believe this!' or maybe you're thinking, 'Wow! I'm going to read for hours every day!'

But I have to say something very important: **you must read books that are easy. You must read books that are fun**[27]**. If a book is too difficult or too boring, put it down and find another one.**

Stephen Krashen, an expert[28] in language teaching, says, 'Only read things in English that are fun and interesting. Read things that are really easy, that you wouldn't read in your native language because they are "too" easy. So you can read comics, magazines, detective stories[29], romance stories[30] and so on. Don't feel bad about reading translations.'[31]

If you read very easy books, when you see a word you don't know, you will understand the meaning easily. You won't have to use a dictionary.

So what is 'easy'? Experiments show that you should understand at least 98%[32] of the words in a text[33].

'98%? That's so high!'

I know. But let me show you an example. Here is a text where 10% of the words are not real words. So you should understand 90% of the words.

Jerry FLURGED out of bed and opened the curtains. He BIMPED to himself as he made breakfast. He made coffee and put butter on his POFFER. Someone called his phone, and he picked it up. He was very surprised by who was TORNGLING, so his VINKY fell on the floor.

Is that easy to understand? Could you read a whole book of that?

Here is the same text, but only 2% of the words are not real. So you should understand 98% of the words:

Jerry jumped out of bed and opened the curtains. He sang to himself as he made breakfast. He made coffee and put butter on his toast. Someone called his phone, and he picked it up. He was very surprised by who was calling, so his VINKY fell on the floor.[34]

How was that?[35] You probably didn't understand everything, but it was more fun to read than the first text. That's why reading for pleasure[36] is so great: maybe you don't understand everything, but you understand enough to follow the story[37], and you don't have to pick up a dictionary!

So if you find that this book is too hard, read something easier. If you find it boring, read something more fun. I know that not everyone likes my writing, and that's OK. Find a book that is good for you. When we have fun, we learn much more.

Because I want this book to be fun, it has no exercises

in it. I thought about adding them after each story, but I don't think it's a good way to spend your time. Instead, you should read more. Read for pleasure. If you finish this book, you can try the level above. Because you already read the stories, you will know them well, and it will be easier to understand.

But maybe when you finish this book you will love stories. I hope so! If you do want to read more, you can listen to my podcast, *Easy Stories in English*. I write a new story every week, with audio[38] and text, and there are over a hundred episodes[39] for you to listen to.

Happy reading and happy learning!

-Ariel Goodbody

THE NORTH WIND AND THE SUN

Nature has many parts. There is water. Water gives us life, and helps us clean ourselves. There is fire. Fire helps us cook food and stay warm. There are trees, which give us fruit and wood. All the parts of nature work together, and help us live on Earth.

*Our planet, Earth (pronunciation **ERTH**)*

There are two parts of nature that are very important. They are the North Wind and the Sun. The North Wind tells us when the weather is going to change. The Sun keeps us warm, and gives us light.

But the North Wind and the Sun are different to the other parts of nature. They do not like to work together. They want to be better than each other. They often think about how they can be better than each other.

The North Wind thinks that being strong is the most

important thing. She thinks that if you are strong, you can do anything. If you can do anything, people will think that you are the best.

The North Wind watches humans. She sees that humans[1] fight[2], and kill, and go to war.

'The humans understand,' says the North Wind. 'The humans understand that being strong is the best thing to be in the world. Because if you are strong, you will win against all others, and everyone thinks you are the best.'

The Sun thinks differently. The Sun does not think that being strong is important. The Sun thinks that the most important thing to be is kind. If you are kind, everyone will like you. If everyone likes you, then you will always have help when you need it. But if you are strong, and not kind, then people will not help you. When you most need help, you will be alone.

The Sun also watches humans. She sees that humans love each other, and make friends and families.

'The humans understand,' says the Sun. 'The humans understand that being kind is the best thing to be in the world. If you are kind, then everyone will love you, and your friends will make you strong.'

One day, the North Wind and the Sun were talking.

'You are weak[3],' said the North Wind. 'You only talk about being kind. What if someone wants to hurt you? If someone wants to steal from you, and you are kind to them, they will simply hurt you[4] and steal from you.'

'Oh, North Wind!' said the Sun. 'It is not so simple. If I

am kind, and I give the person what they want, they will not hurt me.'

'But they will still steal from you!' said the North Wind. 'You will still lose your thing.'

'Things are not everything,' said the Sun. 'People are more important than things.'

'What if the thing is a knife?' said the North Wind. 'A knife is very important. If you have a knife, people will not hurt you.'

'Anyway,' said the Sun, 'if I have lots of friends, and someone steals something from me, it is not important. My friends will help me, and give me the things that I need.'

The North Wind laughed. 'And what will you do when your friends *don't* give you the things that you need?'

The Sun smiled[5]. 'I must hope that they will help me.'

This made the North Wind angry. 'Sun! I will make you understand. Look down there, at the earth.'

The Sun looked down, and saw a man walking along a road. It was winter, and very cold. The man was wearing a big coat.

'This is how we will decide who is better,' said the North Wind. 'We will both try to take off that man's coat. If you can take off the man's coat first, you will win. I will agree that being kind is more important than being strong. But if I take off the man's coat first, I will win. You will have to agree that being strong is more important than being kind.'

The Sun said, 'OK, I will play your game.'

'I will go first,' said the North Wind. 'It will be very simple for me to take off that man's coat.'

The North Wind moved down to the man. She blew[6] very, very hard. The blowing of the wind made a loud sound, *whoosh whoosh*. The trees began to move. They moved very, very quickly. The birds on the trees fell off.

The North Wind blew on the man, because she wanted to push the man's coat off. But the man got colder and colder, so he held his coat tighter and tighter. The more the North Wind blew, the tighter the man held his coat. The man was

This person is holding their coat tightly because it is cold

holding his coat very tightly, and the North Wind could not push it off.

Finally, the North Wind stopped. She could not take off the man's coat.

'Hmm!' the North Wind said. 'I blew as strong as I could. If I could not take off the man's coat, then nobody can. You can try, Sun, but you will not take off his coat.'

The Sun smiled. She was standing behind a cloud, and moved out from behind the cloud. Suddenly[7], the world was full of light. The trees stopped moving. The birds sat on the trees and sang. The cold earth warmed up.

The man saw that it was warm. He stopped holding his coat so tightly. The Sun stood there, and the world got warmer and warmer. So finally, the man took off his coat. He was very happy that it was warm now, and he walked quickly along the road. It got so hot that he stopped, and sat under a tree to rest.

The North Wind said, 'How did you do that?' She was very angry. She could not understand. The Sun had done nothing special. She had not been strong at all. She had just stood there!

The Sun laughed. 'I won by being kind. Being kind is the most important thing in the world. I told you already.'

The North Wind could not believe it. 'I still don't believe that being kind is more important than being strong. You were lucky.'

The Sun smiled. 'You do not have to agree with me. I still love you.'

The North Wind felt very warm, and she could say nothing more.

STRANGE FRIENDS

Once, there were a cat and a mouse. Usually, cats eat mice and mice run away from cats, but this cat and this mouse liked each other very much. They liked each other so much that they lived together. They had a nice little house in the city. Everyone called them the 'strange friends'.

'We must think of winter,' said the cat. 'In winter, it will be cold, and there will be little food. We should save something for winter. You are a mouse, and if you look for food in winter, a cat will eat you.'

A pot

The mouse agreed with the cat. So they bought a pot of fat[1], but they did not know where to put it.

'We can keep it in the house,' the cat said.

'No, no,' said the mouse. 'If we see

it in the house, we will want to eat it. Let us put it in the church, under the big table. Nobody will steal from the church. And if we cannot see it, we will not want to eat it. We will not eat it until we really need it.'

So they put the pot of fat under the big table in the church and went back home. When the mouse thought about the pot of fat, she said, 'Ah, it is good that we have that fat! In winter it will be very good.'

But the cat only thought about herself. A few weeks later, the cat wanted to eat the fat. She thought about how good it would be and she got very hungry.

The cat said to the mouse, 'Dear mouse, I have to ask you something. My cousin has had a beautiful son. He is white and brown. My cousin wants me to be the godmother[2], so I must go to the christening[3]. Will that bother you? You will have to look after the house alone.'

'Of course it won't bother me!' said the mouse. 'Go, and if you find any nice food or drink, bring some for me. At christenings, the wine is very sweet. Bring me some christening wine.'

However, the cat was lying[4]. She had no cousin and nobody had asked her to be a godmother. She went to the church, went under the table, and opened the pot of fat. She ate the top of the fat.

Then she walked on the roofs of the city. She looked for other food and drink but did not see any. So she lay down in the sun. When she thought of the pot of fat, she licked her lips[5] and she came home in the evening.

'I'm sure you have had a lovely day,' said the mouse. 'How was the christening?'

'It went very well,' said the cat.

'What did they name the child?'

'Top-Off,' said the cat.

'Top-Off!' said the mouse. 'That is a very strange name. Do other people in your family have that name?'

'It is not a strange name,' said the cat. 'You have a godchild[6], yes? He is called Big Nose. That is also a very strange name.'

A week later, the cat wanted to eat the fat again. She thought about how good it would be and she got very hungry.

So she said to the mouse, 'You must help me. Again, I have been asked to be godmother. This child has a white ring around its neck and it is very pretty. I cannot say no. Will you look after the house alone while I go to the christening?'

The mouse said yes, but again, the cat went through the city to the church. This time, she ate half the pot of fat. 'Food is much better when you are alone,' she said to herself.

When she went home, the mouse asked, 'What did they name this child?'

'Half-Done,' said the cat.

'Half-Done! Is that true? I have never heard of that name. I don't think it's in the name books!'

A few days later, the cat wanted to eat the fat again.

She thought about how good it would be and she got very hungry.

'Good things come in threes[7],' said the cat to the mouse. 'I have been asked to be godmother again. This child is black, but it has white paws[8]. That is a very strange thing. Will you look after the house while I go to the christening?'

'Top-Off! Half-Done!' said the mouse. 'They are such strange names. They make me think. What name will it be today?'

'You sit at home,' said the cat, 'and you have so many ideas because you do not go out in the day. Well, I will go to the christening and you sit at home and look after the house.'

While the cat was gone, the mouse cleaned the house. She made the house very nice and clean. While the mouse cleaned, the cat ate the whole pot of fat.

'It is good to finish food,' said the cat. She was so full that she did not return home until night-time. The mouse asked what they had named the third child.

'You will not like it,' said the cat. 'He is called All-Gone.'

'All-Gone!' said the mouse. 'That is the strangest name of all. I have never read that name and I have never heard that name. What does it mean?' The mouse asked herself these questions and went to sleep.

After that, nobody asked the cat to be godmother. When winter came, the cat and the mouse didn't have any more food. So the mouse said, 'It is a good thing we have that pot of fat. Let us go to the church, and enjoy our food.'

'Yes,' said the cat to herself. 'Or you could lick[9] the air. You would enjoy it as much.'

'Hmm, what was that?'

'Oh, nothing!'

When they arrived at the church, the pot of fat was there but it was empty.

'Oh no!' said the mouse. 'I see what has happened. I thought we were friends! But you ate all the fat when you were "going to christenings[10]". First Top-Off, then Half-Done, then—'

'Do not finish,' said the cat. When she heard the names she thought of the fat and she was getting very hungry. 'If you say one more word, I will—'

But it was too late. 'All-Gone!' said the mouse. She said the words, and the cat jumped on her and ate her.

Because that is the world. Cats eat mice, and cats get fat.

THE VERY HUNGRY DRAGON

A dragon

Once, there was a very hungry dragon. She was called Grella. Every day, Grella ate five meals. For breakfast she had ten bananas, five eggs and three slices of toast. For her eleven o'clock snack she had twenty chocolate biscuits and three cups of tea. For lunch she had twenty bowls of soup and thirty loaves of bread. After lunch, she was very tired, so she slept for an hour, and when she woke up

*A loaf (pronunciation **LOFE**; plural **loaves**) of bread*

she had some pickles. Finally, for supper she had a roast pig with honey.

This was all good. Grella was a dragon, and dragons

A pickle

are always hungry. But it was strange, because Grella never ate jewels.

'I don't understand!' said Grella's mother.   'Soup and pickles and pig are all good, but you need jewels! Jewels have important vitamins[1] in them.'

A jewel (pronunciation JOO-el)

But Grella *hated* jewels. They were hard, and they tasted of nothing[2]. At every meal, her mother gave her a plate of jewels, but she never ate them. Sometimes, her mother made her eat them, but she spat them out[3] later. So her mother tried changing how the jewels looked. She made them look like vegetables. But Grella smelled[4] them and knew they were not the right food, and threw them on the floor.

One day, Grella's mother got angry.

'Grella, if you don't eat your jewels, then you can't eat anything else.'

She took away the bananas, and the eggs, and the bread and the biscuits and the pickles. She filled every cupboard with fresh jewels, and for every meal the family only had jewels.

'Now, eat your dinner, Grella.'

Grella looked at the plate of emeralds[5] in front of her.

'I won't.' She flew to her room and shut the door.

For a few days, she stayed in her room. Her mother left plates of jewels outside her door but she ignored[6] them. She thought that her mother would get very worried and bring her toast, but this did not happen. For several days, Grella stayed in her room and got more and more hungry.

Finally, she could not stop herself. One night, she went into the kitchen.

She picked up an emerald and looked at it. It just looked so *strange*. But all the other dragons in the world ate them...

Grella ate the emerald. It tasted horrible!

'Eugh[7]!' she said.

But she felt less hungry, so she ate another, and then another.

By the next morning, Grella had eaten all the jewels in the house. Her mother was very happy.

'Wonderful, just wonderful! Wait here, Grella. I will go and get some more jewels for breakfast.'

Her mother brought three bowls of jewels back with her. She said she stole them from a king's castle. It was enough for a whole family for a week. But when Grella's mother wasn't there, Grella ate all of the jewels herself.

'Grella!' said her mother. 'You didn't eat all those jewels, did you?'

'I did,' said Grella. 'And I want more. Where's dessert?'

'Those were all the jewels I got!' said her mother. 'Look, I can go and make some toast if you want.'

But Grella could only think about eating jewels. She needed more, and she needed them *now*.

Grella ran to the window and jumped out, flying away.

'Grella, where are you going?!' shouted her mother. 'It's a school day!'

But Grella didn't hear her. She flew through the air, and far away, she smelled[8] jewels. She followed the smell, flying over the mountains where they lived. Finally, she found a merchant road[9]. On the road, there was a cart.

A cart. The man is carrying things on the cart to sell. Cows are pulling the cart.

And it was full of jewels.

Grella's family had taught her to be a good dragon. She knew that it was bad to kill humans, because then they would come and kill dragons. But she just wanted to have some fun.

She flew down and took the roof off the cart. The merchants saw her and ran away. Grella laughed, and picked up the cart in her hand. She emptied it into her mouth, eating all of the jewels in one go[10].

Grella understood now. Her mother had been right. Jewels were *amazing*. They made her feel wonderful inside, like there was a party inside her stomach.

Grella flew off to find more food.

Grella flew around for a whole week, stealing all kinds of jewels. People soon found out about her. Young dragons thought she was amazing, so they started stealing jewels like her. Of course, the adult dragons thought she was very bad. Grella was giving them a bad reputation[11] and putting herself in danger[12]. Anyway, she should really be in school!

Finally, after eating so many jewels, Grella grew fat and heavy, so she flew home to sleep.

But her mother had different ideas[13].

'Grella, I can't believe you did that!'

'I thought you wanted me to eat jewels?'

'I— I— Not like *this*! I was so worried about you, and now everyone is talking about our family and saying bad things. It was very bad of you!'

Grella's mother shouted at her, but Grella ignored[14] her. She felt very tired, and she could not stop herself from closing her eyes...

When she woke up, it was night. She had no idea how long she had slept, but she was sure it had been a very long time. She knew this because she was very hungry, so it was time to go and eat some jewels.

Grella went to the kitchen and opened the fridge.

No jewels there.

So she went and opened the cupboards.

No jewels there.

She looked in the freezer[15].

No jewels there!

She searched[16] the whole house, but she could not find a jewel anywhere!

But she did find something in her brother's room. He had a secret[17]. Under his bed he had lots of food: pickles and biscuits and chocolate and bread and all sorts of soup. Grella pulled the food out, took it to the kitchen and looked at it.

They were not beautiful like jewels. They smelled strange. Some were hard, but some were really soft. They had all sorts of different colours. Slowly, she picked up a chocolate biscuit and ate it.

Oh, it tasted[18] so good!

Grella started to eat. Several hours later, her parents woke up and came into the kitchen. Almost all the food was gone! Grella lay down on the floor and looked very happy.

'Oh, my daughter!' said her mother. 'My daughter is back!'

She went and hugged[19] Grella, and the young dragon felt a bit sick.

'I don't understand you!' she said. 'First you want me to eat jewels, then you shout at me for it, and now you're happy that I'm eating other food!'

'I know, I know. I'm sorry. I should have never made you change[20].'

She started crying, and hugged Grella again. Mothers were so strange!

'My food!' said Grella's brother. 'Grella, that was my food!'

'Don't worry,' said their mother, drying her eyes. 'From now on[21], we will have *all* kinds of food in this house. There will be jewels for people who want them, and other food for people who want that.'

And so everything was normal again. Every day, Grella ate five meals. For breakfast she had ten bananas, five eggs, and three slices of toast. For her eleven o'clock snack she had twenty chocolate biscuits and three cups of tea. For lunch she had twenty bowls of soup and thirty loaves of bread. After lunch, she was very tired, so she slept for an hour, and when she woke up she had some pickles. Finally, for supper she had a roast pig with honey.

Oh, and sometimes she even ate a jewel.

DOGGO AND KITTY DO THEIR LAUNDRY

Once, there was a dog and a cat. The dog was called Doggo. He had long, thick hair[1]. The cat was called Kitty. She had soft, thin hair. Doggo and Kitty lived together in a small house. Their house was beside a forest. Doggo and Kitty liked living beside the forest very much.

Doggo was only a small dog. Kitty was only a small cat. But they had big dreams. Doggo and Kitty wanted to be like the Big People: the adults. They wanted to walk like adults, talk like adults, and live like adults.

A paw (animal hand) with sharp claws (they can hurt you!)

But there was a problem. Adults have hands, and Doggo and Kitty didn't have hands. They only had paws. Their paws were big, but they weren't like adult hands. They didn't have fingers. They only had sharp claws.

So Doggo and Kitty couldn't be

like the Big People. But they had their dream. Maybe you are thinking: if Doggo and Kitty weren't adults, did they go to school? The answer is no. School is not for animals. School is only for children. Doggo and Kitty were not adults, and they were not children. They were animals. So, of course, they couldn't go to school!

As I said before, Doggo and Kitty lived together in a small house. The house was made of wood and had a red roof. It was a very pretty house. But, because Doggo and Kitty weren't adults, and because they had big paws instead of small hands, they were very messy[2]. Their house was always messy, and they hated cleaning.

One day, Doggo and Kitty were looking for clothes to wear. They liked to wear shirts and trousers and hats, just like the adults did. But Doggo and Kitty couldn't find their clothes! They were not in their draw-ers. They were not in the cupboards.

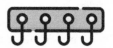

Hooks to put coats on

They were not on the hooks. Finally, Doggo looked on the floor, and he found the clothes there.

'Look, Kitty,' he said. 'Our clothes are all dirty. We can't wear these! Adults don't wear dirty clothes.'

'You're right, Doggo,' said Kitty. 'These clothes are too dirty for us to wear. We will have to wash them.'

'The adults have a word for that, don't they?' said Doggo. 'They call it "laundry[3]".'

'Yes, I think you're right,' said Kitty. 'We are going to have to do our laundry.'

'Very good,' said Doggo. 'Now, how do we do our laundry?'

A woman using a washing board

'It's very simple,' said Kitty. 'You go and get some water, and I will go and get the soap and the washing board.'

'OK then!' said Doggo.

So Doggo went outside to the river with a bucket of water. The bucket was big, wooden and very, very heavy. He took water from the river and put it in the bucket. Kitty opened one of the kitchen cupboards and pulled out a bar of soap. The bar of soap was round, red and very, very pretty. She put it on the table. Then she went to find the washing board. The washing board was a long metal board that they could use to wash the clothes on.

A bucket

Doggo came back to the house, carrying the very heavy bucket of water. He put it on the floor and said, 'Phew!' Then he saw something on the table. It was round, red and very, very pretty.

This must be something very nice, thought Doggo. *It looks very tasty*[4].

Because it looked so tasty, and so pretty, Doggo

thought it must be food. And if it was food, then he should eat it. So Doggo picked up the round, red thing and ate it.

But it wasn't tasty. It was very, very bad!

'Eugh[5]! This is horrible!'

Doggo started coughing[6]. He coughed and coughed. Kitty came back into the kitchen. She saw Doggo coughing and asked, 'Doggo, are you OK? Why are you coughing? Are you sick?'

'No, I'm not sick!' said Doggo. 'I found this red thing here, and I thought it looked very tasty. It looked like a piece of cheese, or maybe some sweets. So I ate it. But it was horrible, and now I can't stop coughing!'

'Doggo!' said Kitty. 'That wasn't food. It was soap! And soap is for washing, *not* for eating.'

'That is why it was so bad!' said Doggo.

'I'm going to get out another bar of soap,' said Kitty, 'but you cannot eat this one! Go and drink some water and wash out your mouth.'

So Doggo went and drank the water from the bucket, and then he had to go and get more water. When he came back, Kitty had found the washing board, and they were all ready to do their laundry[7]. But one thing was missing.

'Wait,' said Doggo. 'We don't have a brush. How can we do our laundry without a brush?'

'I didn't think of that,' said Kitty. 'You're right. Without a brush, we can't rub[8] our clothes on the washing board.'

'Hmm,' said Doggo.

They sat down and thought for a while. Then Kitty jumped in the air.

'Doggo, I have an idea! Brushes have long, thick hair. You also have long, thick hair. We can use *you* as a brush!'

'Good idea!' said Doggo.

So Kitty sat down with the washing board, the bucket of water, and Doggo. She put some dirty clothes on the washing board. Then, she put the soap in the bucket of water and rubbed it on the clothes. Then, she picked up Doggo and rubbed him against the clothes.

Afterwards, they had a pile[9] of clean, wet clothes, and a very dirty, wet Doggo.

'But Kitty,' said Doggo. 'We don't have a towel to dry the clothes with. And I'm too wet to use again.'

'Hmm,' said Kitty.

They sat down and thought for a while. Then Doggo jumped in the air.

'Kitty, I have an idea! Towels have soft, thin hair. You also have soft, thin hair. We can use *you* as a towel!'

'Good idea!' said Kitty.

So Doggo sat down with the pile of clothes and Kitty. He picked up some clothes, put them on the washing board and rubbed Kitty against it.

Afterwards, they had a pile of clean, dry clothes. But Doggo and Kitty were wet and dirty.

'Doggo,' said Kitty, 'if an adult saw us now they would laugh at us! We have done our laundry, but now we need to wash *ourselves*!'

'OK then, Kitty. I will wash you first, and then you will wash me. OK?'

So Kitty climbed onto the washing board, and Doggo started rubbing her with the soap. She shouted, 'Ow!' because he rubbed her very hard. When Doggo was finished, Kitty climbed off the washing board, and Doggo climbed onto it. Kitty started washing him, and he shouted, 'Ow!' because she rubbed him very hard.

Then they both stood up, and squeezed[10] each other, so that all the water in their hair went out onto the floor.

'Now we need to hang ourselves to dry,' said Kitty, 'because we have so much hair. If we stay inside, we will never be dry.'

'You're right,' said Doggo. 'We have to hang ourselves up on the washing line.'

They went into the garden, where the washing line was. They climbed onto the washing line and hung by their

Clothes on a washing line

claws. The sun shone[11] on them.

'The sun is shining on us, Doggo!' said Kitty. 'Soon we will be dry.'

But just when she finished talking, a big cloud came, and it started to rain.

'It's raining!' shouted Doggo. 'Our laundry is getting wet! We must take it down!'

Quickly, they both jumped off the washing line and ran inside the house.

'Is it still raining?' asked Kitty.

'It has stopped,' said Doggo. 'Let's hang up our laundry again.'

So they went into the garden and climbed onto the washing line. The sun shone on them, and they were so happy to see their laundry drying!

But then it started to rain again.

'It's raining!' shouted Kitty. 'Our laundry is getting wet. We must take it down!'

Quickly, they both jumped off the washing line and ran back inside the house. Then the sun shone[12] again, so they went back to the washing line, but then it started to rain again, so they ran back inside the house. They hung from the washing line, ran inside, and went back to the washing line until it was evening, and the sun had stopped shining.

Now they were both clean and dry, but they were very, very tired.

'The laundry is done!' said Doggo.

'What a day!' said Kitty. 'We did our laundry, just like the adults do.'

'So now it's time to go to bed,' said Doggo.

They climbed upstairs and into their beds and quickly went to sleep.

DOGGO AND KITTY TEAR THEIR TROUSERS

Once, there was a dog and a cat. The dog was called Doggo, and the cat was called Kitty. Doggo and Kitty lived together in a small house. Their house was beside a forest, and they liked living there very much.

We have seen how Doggo and Kitty did their laundry[1], so we now know that Doggo and Kitty are very good at keeping their home. There were always lots of things to do in the house. However, the day after they did their laundry was Sunday, and on Sunday you shouldn't do any work. So Doggo and Kitty decided to go out for the day instead. The sun was shining, and they wanted to have a nice day outside.

'Let's go to the forest,' said Doggo. 'When the sun is shining so bright[2], you have to go to the forest.'

'You're right,' said Kitty. 'Since we have done our laundry, let's wear our nice clothes to go out.'

So they got dressed in their nicest clothes to go out into the forest.

'I want a parasol[3],' said Kitty, 'because the bright sun hurts my eyes. And I would be very pretty. I'm sure nobody has seen a pretty kitty like me with a parasol before.'

'I don't think it will hurt you if you get a bit of sun,' said Doggo. 'After the long winter, you're a bit white. You haven't seen the sun for a long time!'

Doggo's words were true. Kitty did look very white because in the winter they sat inside by the fire and didn't see the sun very often.

This dog's ears are uneven, not even. One is up and the other is down.

'Well,' said Kitty, 'you should see how you look. Your ears are uneven. You have one ear up, and the other ear down. Ears should be even.'

'Oh dear! Thank you for telling me, Kitty.'

Doggo made his ears even[4] and they went out of the house. On the way, they talked about what they were going to do in the forest. They were going to play all sorts of games, like hide-and-seek[5]. Doggo was very bad at hide-and-seek. He hid in a bush or a tree, but his ears were always up. Kitty saw his ears and knew where he was. So she liked to play hide-and-seek a lot because she always won.

As they walked, they passed a bush[6] and inside the bush there was a rabbit. The rabbit looked at Doggo and laughed.

'Haha,' said the rabbit, 'that dog has one ear up and the other down! His ears are uneven[7]. Just like this.' And the rabbit made his ears uneven like Doggo. It was true. Doggo had stopped thinking about his ears and they were uneven again.

'Look, that rabbit is laughing at you!' cried Kitty.

Doggo got very angry and ran after the rabbit. He jumped into the bush, but the rabbit was much faster than him and ran away.

'Oh, there are so many thorns in this bush!' cried Doggo. 'I should not have run after that rabbit.'

'Those thorns didn't really hurt you, did they?' said Kitty.

'No, not really,' said Doggo.

Doggo made his ears even again and they continued on their way. A few minutes later, they met some of the children who lived on the other side of the forest.

There are thorns on this rose. They are sharp and can hurt you.

'Hello, Doggo and Kitty!' said the children. 'Since it's so sunny today, we decided to go for a walk in the forest.'

'We decided the same thing,' said Kitty.

'You are dressed in very pretty clothes,' said children.

Then they looked again and started to laugh. Doggo

thought it was because of his ears, but he checked and they were even, not uneven.

'Look, boys! Look, girls! Doggo has torn[8] his trousers!'

'The children say that I have a tear in my trousers,' said Doggo. 'Please look and see, Kitty.'

So Kitty looked at Doggo carefully. 'I'm afraid it's true. Your trousers are torn.'

A needle and thread. You use them to make clothes.

'That probably happened when I ran into that bush[9], which had so many thorns in it,' said Doggo. 'I can't believe I have torn my nicest trousers. What a shame! Kitty, do you have a needle and thread?'

'I'm afraid I don't. But maybe we will find something on the way, a piece of string or something like that.'

So they said goodbye to the children, who were still laughing a lot, and continued on their way[10].

String

'Hey, look!' said Doggo. 'I see something.'

A worm

On the ground, there was a worm. The worm was sleeping in the afternoon sun, thinking that nobody could see it.

'It's long, thin and straight,' said Doggo. 'I think it is a pencil.'

The worm woke up. It saw Doggo

and was afraid, so it curled up into a circle.

'No, that's no pencil!' said Kitty. 'It has curled up into a circle. So I think it is a piece of string. What luck! I will take it and use it to mend[11] your trousers.'

When you curl up, you move into this shape.

So Kitty picked up the worm and used it to mend the tear[12] in Doggo's trousers.

'There, now nobody can laugh at me,' said Doggo.

They continued on their way and talked about all the places that they would hide in later when they played hide-and-seek. The worm was surprised and afraid when Kitty used him to mend the trousers, so it did nothing. But now it was no longer surprised and said to itself, 'I'm no piece of string, I'm a worm.' And it slowly began to move.

As the worm moved, Doggo and Kitty met a friend. It was Clucky the chicken.

'Hello, Clucky!' said Doggo and Kitty.

'Hello, Doggo and Kitty. Doggo! There is something on your leg. It's a worm!'

As Clucky was a chicken, she loved to eat worms, so she tried to eat it. The worm fell off Doggo's trousers and ran away into the forest.

'How strange,' said Clucky. 'It was coming out of a hole[13] in your trousers. I didn't know worms ate trousers. It's very bad to eat people's trousers! I really wanted to eat that worm. Then he would know that it's bad to eat people's trousers.'

'Yes, what a shame!' said Doggo. But really, he was glad that Clucky didn't catch the worm, because he hated violence[14].

'Oh, Doggo!' said Kitty, who was looking at his trousers again. 'Your trousers are torn again. That was the string, not a worm!'

'No way,' said Clucky. 'That was a worm, I'm sure. String doesn't move and curl up like that! Yes, it was a worm, 100%, and I wanted very much to eat it! But you don't need to worry, Doggo. I don't have a needle and thread, but if you continue on your way, you will come to a house where a seamstress[15] works. The seamstress can mend[16] your trousers for you.'

So they said goodbye to Clucky and continued on their way to the seamstress's house.

'Wow, that's a big tear,' said the seamstress. 'But it's a Sunday, and you shouldn't work on Sundays. Maybe if you do some work for me I will mend it for you. I have lots of mice in my kitchen. If you send away all the mice, I will mend your trousers. But you cannot drink the milk and eat the biscuits that are on the table!'

Doggo and Kitty said that they would catch the mice and leave the milk and biscuits. The seamstress showed them the kitchen. The mice were afraid of Doggo and Kitty and hid[17] in their holes[18].

'I will go outside,' said Kitty. 'Go stand in front of their holes, Doggo.'

So Doggo went and stood in front of the mice's holes.

Kitty went outside, and said, 'Yay! There is a dog inside with one ear up and the other down. And he has torn a hole in his trousers. How funny he looks!'

The mice, who loved to laugh, ran out of their holes to laugh at the dog. Doggo jumped on them and caught them under his paw[19].

'Oh no!' cried the mice. 'Are you going to eat us?'

'No, I hate violence[20]. But you must leave the seamstress's house and never come back.'

The mice said that they would never come back and then ran away, still laughing about Doggo's trousers.

'Well done!' said the seamstress, when she came back into the kitchen.

She mended the tear in Doggo's trousers. Then Doggo and Kitty sat down and drank a glass of milk and ate some biscuits, which were very nice.

Afterwards, they walked home through the forest. They were too tired to play hide-and-seek. That evening, they slept very well, but Doggo's ears were uneven through all the night.

DOGGO AND KITTY BAKE A CAKE

Once, there was a dog and a cat. The dog was called Doggo, and the cat was called Kitty. Doggo and Kitty lived together in a small house. Their house was beside a forest, and they liked living there very much.

One day, Kitty looked at their calendar.

'Doggo!' said Kitty. 'The calendar says that today is my birthday.'

'Yay!' said Doggo. 'We will have to celebrate[1]. But how? I have never celebrated a birthday before.'

Kitty thought that they *had* celebrated a birthday before. She thought that birthdays happened every year. But she wasn't sure, so she didn't say anything.

'Yes, we must celebrate! But what should we do?'

While Doggo and Kitty were thinking of how to celebrate Kitty's birthday, some other people were thinking the same thing. The children who lived on the other side of the forest liked Doggo and Kitty very much. They wanted to give Kitty a surprise on her birthday, so they decided to bake her a big cake.

The problem was, they didn't have the ingredients[2] for a cake. Usually for a cake you need flour, milk and eggs, and all sorts of other things. These are things that children don't know about. So they used what they could find.

*Flour (pronunciation **FLAU-er**) is a white powder that you use to cook bread, pasta, cakes and so on.*

First, they took a cake tin. It was a big, round metal thing that they would cook the cake in. Then, they put in sand[3], because cake is soft like sand. But the sand was too soft, so they poured[4] in water and mixed the water with the sand. This was difficult, and they got lots of sand on the floor. Finally, they took some small, white stones and

A cake tin and a cake

put them on top of the cake, because nice cakes always had nuts on top, and the stones looked like nuts. Then they put the cake tin in the oven and waited for an hour. They didn't turn the oven on, because only their parents could do that.

Stones at the beach

Nuts

*An oven (pronunciation **UH-vun**)*

Out of the oven came a beautiful cake. The children thought it looked amazing. They wanted to try it, but they knew that they couldn't, because it was for Kitty. So they carried it through the forest to the small wooden house where Doggo and Kitty lived.

'Hello, Doggo and Kitty!' the children said. 'We made you a cake and brought it here to celebrate Kitty's birthday.'

'What a nice surprise!' Kitty said. 'We were thinking about how to celebrate. This is perfect!'

'The cake is really, really nice,' the children said. 'You will love it.'

So they all went and sat down in the kitchen. Doggo and Kitty soon saw that the cake was actually horrible. Nobody could eat such a cake. But they liked the children very much, so they cut up the cake and put slices on plates. They held the cake slices under their noses and smelled[5] them and said, 'Yum yum!' The children looked at them, so they pretended[6] to eat the slices of cake. The children laughed and pretended to eat their slices as well.

'Thank you so much, children,' said Kitty. 'We have never had such a delicious[7] cake before.'

The children laughed and went home. Doggo and Kitty then took the plates of cake to the river outside and threw them into the water.

'It was nice of the children to do that for us,' said Doggo. 'But now I really *am* hungry. I would like to eat some cake, I think. But it has to be real!'

'Me too. I would also like to eat a real cake,' said Kitty. 'Well, since it's my birthday, why don't we bake one? The only problem is, I don't know how to bake a cake.'

'I know, I know! It's very easy, Kitty. All you do is add your favourite food to the cake. When you add five delicious things, then the cake will be five times as good[8]. When you add ten delicious things, then the cake will be ten times as good. So if we add a *hundred* delicious things, then the cake will be a hundred times as good!'

'That's true!' said Kitty. 'We are going to make the most delicious cake ever.'

So Doggo and Kitty took out their cake tin and got ready to cook.

First, they took flour, milk and eggs, and mixed them in a large bowl. The children didn't put those in their cake, but Doggo and Kitty knew that you had to have flour, milk and eggs in a cake.

'The cake must be sweet,' said Kitty, and she poured[9] a kilogram of sugar into the bowl.

'And a bit salty as well,' said Doggo, and he poured a bit of salt into the bowl.

'And let's add some butter and jam,' said Kitty.

'Not jam,' said Doggo. 'I don't like jam. Let's add some cheese. I love cheese.'

So they added some cheese to the bowl.

*Bacon (pronunciation **BAY-kun**), a type of pig meat*

'I think that we need something greasy[10] in it,' said Kitty. 'Let's add some bacon.'

So they added a slice of bacon to the bowl.

'And we can't forget nuts!' said Doggo.

So he poured some nuts into the bowl.

'Nuts are good,' said Kitty, 'but if we are adding nuts then we should also add some cucumber.'

So she cut up a cucumber and put it in the bowl, too.

'And bones!' said Doggo. 'We must add some bones, as well! They are the most delicious food in the world.'

So they added some bones to the mix.

'And we must add some mice!' said Kitty. 'Mice are my favourite food.'

So they added five mice into the bowl.

*A type of cucumber (pronunciation **KYOO-kum-buh**)*

'Oh,' said Doggo, 'and let's add some sausages for me.'

So they added some sausages to the bowl.

'And we can't forget cream!' said Kitty. 'We must add some cream.'

So they poured a litre of cream into the bowl.

A bone

'And a bit of garlic,' said Doggo.

So they put a few pieces of garlic into the bowl.

'And chocolate,' said Kitty.

So they added a piece of chocolate to the bowl.

They added everything they liked to the bowl, which was all the food they had in the house. They mixed and mixed and it took a long time because there was so much food.

'This is going to be an excellent cake!' said Doggo. 'And now we just have to bake it.'

They put the cake in the oven for an hour. The children could not turn the oven on, but Doggo and Kitty could, because they had no parents to stop them. When the cake was baked, they put it by the window. They opened the window so that the cake could cool[11].

'You know what?' said Kitty. 'Since the children were nice enough to bring us a cake, I think we should give them some cake as well.'

'Good idea,' said Doggo. 'Let's go find them.'

So they went through the forest to find the children.

While they walked, a very naughty[12] dog went past their house. As the cake was cooling, its smell[13] went through the trees. The dog smelled it, and he had never smelled such a delicious thing.

'That smells like the most delicious thing in the world!' the dog said to himself. 'I have to find it.'

The dog followed the smell until he found a small wooden house with a cake cooling by the window. The cake smelled so good that the dog's eyes were watering[14]. His mouth was watering, too.

The dog jumped up and ate the cake. It was so delicious that he ate it all in seconds. Then the dog went and drank some water from the river, and sat down by a big tree.

The cake had been *so* delicious, but the dog's stomach felt *so* bad. It hurt more than it had ever hurt before.

'What was in that cake?' the dog asked himself.

When Doggo and Kitty returned with the children, the cake was gone. They were very sad, and very surprised. What had happened to the cake?

'Look!' said one of the children. 'There's a big dog over there, with a stomach as big as me. I think he ate the cake.'

The naughty dog didn't get up and run away, because his stomach hurt too much.

'I'm sorry,' he said. 'It smelt so good. I couldn't stop myself from eating it.'

'Don't worry,' said Kitty. 'I don't think the cake was good at all, because your stomach is hurting so much. I am happy we didn't eat it! If we had eaten it, our stomachs would have hurt and my birthday would have been terrible. I'm glad you ate it instead.'

'Well, I'm not glad!' said the dog, and they all laughed.

'There's just one problem,' said Doggo. 'We put all the food in our house into that cake, and now we have nothing to eat, and we are very hungry.'

'Not to worry, Doggo and Kitty,' said the children. 'Come and eat dinner at our house. We will make mud[15] pie[16] for dessert.'

So Doggo and Kitty went to eat at the children's house. They had soup, chicken and bones. They enjoyed it very much. They didn't eat the mud pie, but they pretended to eat it. And the naughty dog sat and cried all night, because his stomach hurt from the horrible cake which Doggo and Kitty had baked.

SLEEPING BEAUTY

Far away from our world, there were the Blue Castle and the Red Castle. In the Blue Castle, everything was soft and blue, and Izod was the softest fairy of all. Izod loved her land[1], and the land loved her. It was a happy place, but at times it was very sad.

A fairy is a girl with wings who can use magic

When one of the High Fairies died, all the people cried for days. Izod cried more than everyone else. She had a big heart and beautiful wings[2]. They called them her 'wings of water'.

Because of this, she was chosen to be queen. She was afraid at first, but she was also excited. She had to wait until she became sixteen. But on the day of her sixteenth birthday, the men from the Red Castle came.

It was the first time that Izod had seen them. They wore red. Their eyes were red like fire. And when they attacked[3], the Blue Castle turned red with blood. They killed and killed, and Izod cried and cried. When they found her, she had cried every tear[4] from her body.

But the Red Men did not kill her. They did something much worse. They hit her, pulled out her wings, and left her alone in the Blue Castle. All alone.

Her beauty[5] was dead, and her magic was gone.

Della loved her land, and the land loved her. Her father and mother, the King and Queen, smiled[6] every time they saw her. She had beautiful red hair. People called it her 'hair of fire'. The people of the Red Castle brought her presents every day. In the Red Castle, everything was bright, and everyone was strong, and Della was also bright and strong. When a gladiator[7] killed another man, she shouted, 'Hooray! Well done!' She would be queen one day, and she would be a strong queen.

But on Della's sixteenth birthday, everything changed.

The day started with beautiful sunshine but quickly turned dark and wet. Many people had come for Della's birthday, and now they all stood inside the castle. They were wet and cold, but still, they were happy for Della.

Della sat and received the people's presents. There were many things: cakes, jewellery, paintings and dresses. Finally, Sir Galen came up. He was the head of the guards[8]. He wore bright red clothes and he was very strong and handsome[9]. He gave Della a very interesting present.

'These are wings. They are from a fairy, and they have strong magic. I wanted to give them to you before but you were too young. Be careful with them. They are dangerous.'

And then, the doors to the Red Castle opened by themselves. A strong wind and heavy rain came in.

'Shut those doors!' shouted the Queen.

The guards did so, but with the wind, something had come inside. Not something, but someone. It was a tall person, wearing a black cloak. Their face was hidden. It could not be seen. The people were afraid and moved away from the cloaked person, who moved forward.

*A cloak (pronunciation **CLOKE**) is a big piece of clothing that you wear outside*

'Who are you?' asked the Queen.

The person took off the cloak. It was a woman, but she looked very bad. Her face was dark blue, and her eyes were as white as milk. She looked soft and sad. She looked like the rain turned into a person.

Della had heard of the Blue Castle and the strange blue fairies who lived there. But they had all died, years ago. That was what her parents had told her.

The woman looked at Della. 'Give me back my wings. I need them to fly.'

This person is moving forwards, because they can see where they are going. If they were moving backward, they could not see.

She was quiet, but nobody in the castle spoke a word. Della was afraid but she did not show it.

'These are not your wings,' she said. 'Sir Galen gave them to me.'

The blue woman just shook her head[10]. 'Those wings are mine. Give me back my wings. I need them to fly.'

'Guards!' said the King. 'Take this woman!'

But the guards did not move. In fact, nobody in the room moved. Nobody *could* move.

The blue woman said again, 'Give me back my wings. I need them to fly.' She sounded like she was going to cry.

Della stood up. She picked up the wings and looked at them. They were hers because they were a present from Sir Galen. But this woman, this strange woman, wanted them so much. Della knew that if she didn't give her the wings, her birthday would be bad. So she walked towards[11] her.

'No!' shouted Sir Galen. 'It is Izod, the bad fairy of the Blue Castle!'

Della stopped. There was a moment of quiet and then the blue woman's face changed. Her face turned angry. She tried to move towards the wings, but the guards ran forward. They held her back.

'Then she will suffer[12] like me!' shouted the blue

woman. 'If I cannot fly, then she must sleep. Tonight, she will fall asleep[13] and she will never wake up again.'

Then, Izod was gone. The cloak fell to the floor. The Red Castle was quiet. Outside, the sun shone again.

That night, Della did not sleep. She also did not sleep the next night. Every night for a week, she did not sleep. The King and Queen found entertainers—musicians[14], clowns and dancers—to stop her from sleeping. But each day, Della grew more tired, and one night, she fell asleep at the dinner table.

The King and Queen tried to wake her up. They shook[15] her. They brought delicious[16] food and drinks. Musicians played music. But nothing worked, so they carried her to bed. The King and Queen sat by her every night and told stories. But finally, they were suffering too much, and even they left her.

Della lay alone in her room. She was a sleeping beauty, and nothing more.

∽

I zod slept as well. Without her wings, her magic was not strong. To keep Della asleep, she had to sleep as well.

In their dreams, they met. At first, Della ran away. But as the years passed, she could not keep doing this. Finally, they talked.

'Why did you do this?' Della asked. She did not sound

like a child anymore. She was a suffering woman now, just like Izod.

'I had nothing left.'

Della shook her head. 'But you got nothing from this. Now we are both asleep. You do not have your wings. Does it make you happy, to see me suffer?'

'Of course it doesn't. I know how you are suffering. I feel your pain.'

Della started to cry. She could not stop the tears[17] any longer. 'Then why did you do this?'

'You know the history of our lands.'

Della could not look in Izod's eyes. It was true. Her people had gone to the Blue Castle and killed them. They had killed families and killed the land. And they had taken Izod's wings. 'I know it was wrong. But being queen is not easy. My mother has to do many things she doesn't want to do. And your people were dangerous. You had magic.'

'One time, we all had magic.' Izod smiled. 'But they did not tell you that story, did they? One time, we were all one. Blue and Red were together. And then we broke ourselves up[18] and killed one side of ourselves.'

Della shook her head again. 'I don't understand.'

'There is a way to wake up, but you will not like it. But it is my only hope. It is the reason I did this.'

'Tell me.'

≈

Della woke up, but she was not Della now. She was Izodella. She had her wings of water, and she had her hair of fire.

Her mother and father were dead now and Sir Galen was king. The land was Red, red with fire and blood. There was no happiness, only suffering.

Izodella did not wait. She killed the king. Then she flew above the land. She held out her right hand, and fire rained down. It ate the Red Castle and the Blue Castle. It killed everything and all. Then she held out her left hand, and water rained down. It cleaned the land and ended the suffering.

The fires died and the rain stopped. The land slept. Izodella cried, and her tears fell on the earth[19]. And where they fell, something new woke up.

Green.

ONE-EYED, TWO-EYED, THREE-EYED

There was once an old woman who had three daughters. The oldest daughter had three eyes, so she was called Three-Eyed. The youngest daughter had one eye, so she was called One-Eyed. The middle daughter had two eyes, so she was called Two-Eyed.

Three-Eyed was beautiful, and One-Eyed was very clever, but Two-Eyed was not clever or beautiful. However, she did work very hard[1]. Her sisters hated her because she had two eyes like normal people, and her mother hated her because she was not special like her sisters.

One day, the mother decided that it was time for her daughters to get married.

'Three-Eyed will get married to a rich businessman, because she is so beautiful. One-Eyed will get married to a doctor, because she is so clever.'

'And who will I get married to, Mother?' asked Two-Eyed.

'Nobody!' she cried. 'You will not get married to anyone. You will stay at home and look after your mother.'

So the old woman prepared her oldest and youngest daughters to get married. She painted a second eye on One-Eyed's face, so that she had two eyes. Then she took some horse hair and made a fringe[2] to put on Three-Eyed's head, so that people could not see her third eye.

'There!' she said. 'Now everyone will want to marry[3] you!'

A few days later, a man came round looking for a wife.

'Come in, come in!' said the old woman. 'Perhaps you would like to marry my oldest daughter, who is very pretty?'

The man looked at Three-Eyed and said, 'Hmm, I think not.'

'Well, perhaps you would prefer my youngest daughter? She is very clever.'

The man saw One-Eyed and said, 'No, I do not like her. Where is the middle daughter?'

'Oh no, she is not beautiful or clever. You do not want to marry her.'

Two-Eyed was in the next room. She had seen the man through the window, and he looked very nice. So she walked into the room.

'Hello,' she said.

'Ah! *This* is the daughter I want to marry.'

'No, no!' said the mother. 'She does not want to get married.'

'But Mother, I—'

'Goodbye!'

And the mother pushed the man out of the door and shut it. Suddenly[4], the old woman, Three-Eyed and One-Eyed all turned on Two-Eyed.

'You think you are so clever, don't you?' said the mother. 'You cannot get married. I already told you.'

'You are not beautiful!' said Three-Eyed.

'Or clever!' said One-Eyed.

Two-Eyed started crying, and ran to her bed.

The mother and the two favourite daughters thought about what to do. They needed to make sure that no man wanted to marry Two-Eyed.

'I have an idea!' said the mother. 'We will give her less food and make her work hard[5] in the fields. She will be hungry and sad. She will get thin, and her skin[6] will go hard. Nobody will want to marry her!'

So early the next day, Three-Eyed and One-Eyed pulled Two-Eyed out of bed, and told her she had to work in the fields.

'What about breakfast?' she asked.

'No breakfast for you, lazy!' said Three-Eyed.

So the girl went to the field and started working. It was a beautiful day, and she did not mind working hard, because her lunch would be even better afterwards.

A few hours later, a goat[7] came to her.

'Meeeh! Good day, Two-Eyed.'

'How do you know my name?' the girl asked. 'And, oh! How can you talk?'

'I am not a normal goat and you are not a normal girl.'

'Oh, but I am normal. I am not beautiful like my older sister, and I am not clever like my younger sister. And I only have two eyes, just like you and most people.'

'Oh no, you are special. You just do not know it yet. But that is not important. I think you are hungry.'

'Yes, I am quite hungry. But when I finish working, we will have lunch, I am sure.'

'No!' said the goat. 'They will give you very little food. They made a plan last night. They will give you very little food, so that you get thin and your skin goes hard.'

'Oh!' said the girl.

'But do not worry. As I said, I am not a normal goat. Say these magic words and I will help you: "Little goat, little goat, it's time to eat." When you are done, say, "Little goat, little goat, it's time to go." '

So the girl said, 'Little goat, little goat, it's time to eat.'

Suddenly[8], the goat started changing. It grew long and square, and became a big white table. And on the table were all

A pickle

kinds of food: bread, cheeses, jams, pickles, tomatoes, olives, and so on. The girl was hungry from the work, so she ate lots and lots of food, and when she was done, she said, 'Little goat, little goat, it's time to go.'

Green olives

The table became a goat again.

'See you tomorrow, Two-Eyed!' he said, and ran away.

When Two-Eyed finished her work and came home, lunch was ready.

'I suppose you want to eat?' said the mother.

'No, thank you!' said Two-Eyed. 'I ate lots of food yesterday.'

For several days, the mother and her two favourite daughters sent Two-Eyed into the fields to work, and she ate food from the goat's table, and she ate no food at home. The three horrible women thought and thought. Why did she not eat? Why was she not thin?

Finally, the mother said, 'Enough! Tomorrow, One-Eyed, you will go with your sister into the field and find out what is happening. I am sure she is stealing that food from somewhere.'

So the next day, One-Eyed went with Two-Eyed to the fields. But the younger sister did not want to work with Two-Eyed, so they sat down together and watched the sky.

'Sister, sing me a song,' said One-Eyed.

So Two-Eyed started to sing.

'Sister, sister, are you asleep[9]?

Or are you awake[10]? Tell me, tell me.'

'I am awake,' said One-Eyed.

'Sister, sister, are you asleep?

Or are you awake? Tell me, tell me.'

'I am awake,' said One-Eyed.

Two-Eyed continued to[11] sing, and her voice[12] went

quiet. Finally, One-Eyed's eye closed and she fell asleep. Then, Two-Eyed got up, went and found the goat.

'Little goat, little goat, it's time to eat!'

The goat became a table, and the girl ate and ate, while her sister slept and slept. Then she said, 'Little goat, little goat, it's time to go!'

The goat went away, and Two-Eyed went and woke up her sister.

'Come on, sister! It is time to go home.'

'Oh!' said One-Eyed. 'Did I sleep for that long?'

That evening, their mother and Three-Eyed asked One-Eyed what she saw, but the girl told them that she slept and saw nothing.

'That was not the plan!' said her mother.

'Actually, I did see one thing!' One-Eyed said. 'When she woke me up, she had some cheese on her mouth.'

'Hmm,' said the mother. 'Tomorrow, Three-Eyed, you will go with her to the fields. And you must be more careful than your sister!'

So the next day, Two-Eyed and Three-Eyed went to the fields.

'Sister, sing me a song,' said Three-Eyed.

So they sat down, and Two-Eyed started to sing.

'Sister, sister, are you asleep?

Or are you awake? Tell me, tell me.'

'I am awake,' said Three-Eyed.

'Sister, sister, are you asleep?

Or are you awake? Tell me, tell me.'

'I am awake,' said Three-Eyed.

Two-Eyed continued to[13] sing, and her voice[14] went quiet. Finally, Three-Eyed's eyes closed. Then, Two-Eyed carefully got up, went and found the goat.

But Three-Eyed was not asleep. Her two lower eyes were closed, but under her fringe[15], her third eye was open. Carefully, she moved the fringe and watched what Two-Eyed was doing.

Her bottom eyes were closed, but her third eye was open

'Little goat, little goat, it's time to eat!'

Three-Eyed saw the goat become a table, and she saw Two-Eyed eat her meal. Then the girl said, 'Little goat, little goat, it's time to go!'

That evening, Three-Eyed told her mother and sister everything that had happened. Her mother had never looked so happy before.

'I have an idea,' she said. 'Tonight, we will have goat for supper.'

'Yes,' said Three-Eyed, 'but what about the magic goat?'

'We are going to *eat* the magic goat.'

'*Oh.*'

When Two-Eyed heard this, she started crying, and she cried and cried all day. Then she slept in her room, and had a strange dream.

In the dream, she was working in the fields, but the goat did not come to her. Instead, an old man visited.

'They are going to eat the goat,' he said.

'What can I do?' said Two-Eyed.

'After the meal is finished, take the goat's hooves and horns. Dig a hole[16] behind the door and put them in the hole. But make sure that nobody sees.'

*Some animals have hard feet called hooves (singular **hoof**)*

So that evening, the mother and her

Some animals have sharp things on their heads called horns

two favourite daughters ate goat curry for supper. Two-Eyed sat outside and watched them through the window, but the girl did not cry.

After the meal was finished, the old woman said, 'Two-Eyed, clean up the hooves and horns.'

Two-Eyed waited until they were in bed, then she dug a hole and planted the hooves and horns inside. After that, she was very tired and went to bed.

The next day, a beautiful apple tree had grown by the door. And it was no normal apple tree; the apples were made of gold!

'Daughters, daughters!' said the mother. 'Look, it's amazing!'

But when she tried to pick[17] the apples, the tree moved away, and she could not pick them. As Three-Eyed was the tallest, her mother told her to pick them, but again, the tree moved away and Three-Eyed could not pick the apples. So One-Eyed stood on Three-Eyed's head, but the same thing happened—the tree moved away—and they both fell.

'I hate this!' said One-Eyed. 'Those are our golden apples!'

The mother looked at Two-Eyed and said, 'Don't think about picking any of those apples. They are my apples, not yours.'

But when they were not looking, Two-Eyed tried picking an apple. The tree moved down to her, and she easily picked one of the beautiful golden apples. She put it in her dress and went back to work.

A few days later, the man from before came round again.

'I still want to marry your middle daughter,' he said. 'Are you sure that she does not want to get married?'

'Yes, yes!' said the mother. 'But it does not matter. The horrible little girl ran away.'

Actually, Two-Eyed was under the bed, because her mother had told her to go there. She did not want the man to see her.

'Oh, what a beautiful tree you have! Those apples are amazing,' said the man.

He thought for a moment, and decided that Three-Eyed and One-Eyed could be good wives, but they had to work hard.

'Can your lovely daughters pick me some apples?'

So the mother sent Three-Eyed and One-Eyed to the tree, but they could not pick a single apple[18].

'How funny,' the man said. He did not sound happy.

Two-Eyed knew she had to do something. So she waited until the man was inside again, and then she threw the golden apple from under the bed. The man looked down and saw it.

'Oh! Here is one of the apples.' He picked it up. 'But where did it come from...?'

'I don't know!' said the mother. 'I suppose Three-Eyed picked it earlier.'

The man looked around, and he saw some eyes under the bed. He went down and pulled out Two-Eyed.

'Ah, your daughter has not run away!' he said. 'Your mother says that you do not want to get married. Is this true?'

'No, no!' said Two-Eyed. 'I would love to marry you.'

'Wonderful!' said the man. 'Let's go and get married right now.'

'No, you can't go!' said the mother. 'That was not the plan!'

But Two-Eyed and her new husband did not hear her, and walked out of the house. They stopped in the garden.

'I suppose you want me to pick you some apples?' said Two-Eyed. She wanted to show him that she could work hard.

'Oh no,' he said. 'You are the perfect wife. I just know it.'

So they went and got married, and lived happily together. And the mother and her two favourite daughters never picked an apple from the tree.

THE BOY WHO KNEW NO FEAR

Once, there was a father. He had two sons. The older son, Hugh, was clever and could do everything, but the younger son, Anders, was stupid[1] and understood nothing. When the father needed help, the older son always helped him, and the younger son did nothing.

But sometimes, the father asked Hugh to go somewhere late at night, and the son was afraid and said, 'Oh no, Father, I'm afraid! I can't go out in the night. It makes me shudder[2].' And when their father told scary[3] stories, Hugh said, 'Oh, it makes me shudder!'

Anders sat and listened, but he did not understand. 'He is always saying, "It makes me shudder, it makes me shudder!" It does not make *me* shudder. I do not understand what that means.'

One day, the father said to Anders, 'Listen to me. You are growing up. You are big and strong. You must learn something and get a job. Look at your brother. He works hard while you sit and do nothing.'

'Actually, Father,' he said, 'I do want to learn something. I want to learn how to shudder. I don't understand it.'

Hugh laughed and said, 'God, what a stupid[4] brother I have! He will never do anything good.'

The father said, 'You can easily learn how to shudder, but you will not find a job like that.'

A few days later, a priest came to visit the house. The father told him about the problem with Anders. 'When I asked him what job he wanted to do, he said he wanted to learn to shudder!'

A priest (pronunciation PREEST), a person who works in the Catholic church

'He wants to learn how to shudder?' said the priest. 'Well, he can learn it from me. He can come and live with me, and I will teach him how to shudder.'

So Anders went to live in the priest's house. The priest taught him to ring the bell in the church, and every day he rang it. After a few days, the priest woke up in the night, and told Anders to go and ring the bell. *You will soon learn to shudder...* he thought, and went up to the bell before Anders.

The boy wanted to ring the bell, but then he saw a man wearing white. The man was standing at the top of the stairs.

'Who is there?' he said.

But the man in white did not say anything. Anders thought it was a ghost.

'Answer me,' said Anders, 'or leave. I have to ring the bell.'

The priest did not move. *I will not move. Then, the boy will think I am a ghost,* thought the priest.

A man ringing a bell

'What do you want here?' shouted Anders. 'Say something, or I will throw you down the stairs!'

The priest thought, *He doesn't really mean that.* He did not move.

*A ghost (pronunciation **GOSTE**), the spirit of a dead person*

Because the ghost did not move, Anders ran and pushed it down the stairs. The ghost fell down and shouted. Then Anders rang the bell and went to bed.

The priest's wife waited for her husband. She waited a long time. Finally, she woke up Anders and asked, 'Do you know where my husband is? He went up to the bell before you.'

'No, I don't know,' said the boy, 'but someone was standing up there in white. He did not answer me or leave, so I thought he was a ghost and threw him down the stairs.'

The woman ran up to the bell and found her husband. He was crying on the floor, and had broken his leg.

The next day, the priest's wife went to Anders' father and shouted, 'Your boy has given us great problems! He threw my husband down the stairs and broke his leg. We don't want him anymore.'

The father went to Anders and said, 'What did you do, you stupid boy?!'

'Father,' said Anders, 'I did nothing wrong. That man stood there in a strange way. He wanted to do something bad. I asked him three times who he was, and he did not answer. So I threw him down the stairs.'

'I have nothing to say to you! Leave. I will not have you in this house anymore.'

'Of course, Father,' said Anders. 'I will go out and learn how to shudder.'

But the father did not hate his son, so he gave him some money, and said, 'Don't tell anyone who your father is.'

'Of course, Father.'

For a while, Anders walked around. He said many times, 'If only I could shudder[5]!'

A few hours later, he walked past a tree. Seven men were hanged on the tree. Another man saw Anders.

That boy looks very stupid, he thought. *I think I will have some fun with him.*

So he went and spoke to Anders.

'Hello there! Where are you going?'

'I'm going to learn how to shudder,' said Anders.

The man laughed. 'I can teach you how to shudder! Look at that tree. Seven men wanted to get married to a man's daughter, but the man did not like this. Now they are learning how to fly. Sit by the tree and wait for the night. By the morning, you will have learned how to shudder.'

Hanging is an old way to kill people. People were hanged on ropes like this.

'Wow, it's that easy? Well, if I do learn, I will give you all my money.'

'Perfect. Sweet dreams!'

So Anders went and sat by the tree and waited for the night. Because it was cold, he made a fire. There was a cold wind, and the hanged men moved in the wind.

'You must be cold[6] up there!' said Anders.

So he climbed up the tree and cut down the seven men. He put them by the fire, but they did not move. So he pushed them closer. The fire started burning[7] their clothes, but still they did not move.

'Wow, you really are quite stupid!' said Anders. 'I should put you back up there.'

The dead men did not say anything, and their clothes burned more. This made Anders quite angry.

'It is dangerous! Your clothes are burning. Stupid men!'

So he put them back on the tree, and then went and slept by the fire.

The next day, the man came and asked him, 'Well, did you learn how to shudder?'

'No! Those men were so stupid. They said nothing, and their clothes burned on the fire! How could I learn to shudder from them?'

So Anders walked more, always saying, 'If only I could shudder[8]!'

Another man heard him and asked, 'Who are you?'

'I don't know,' said Anders.

'Where are you from?'

'I forgot.'

'Who is your father?'

'I cannot tell you.'

'And what did you say before?'

'I said, "If only I could shudder!" You see, I want to learn to shudder.'

'I know who can teach you. But I want money.'

'OK!' said Anders, and he gave the man all his money.

'There is a castle near here. No man lives there. Only ghosts and strange animals live in it. If you stay in the castle for three nights, you will learn how to shudder. The King has said that if someone stays in the castle for three nights, they can get married to his daughter. She is the most beautiful woman in the world. There is also lots of gold in the castle. If you stay there three nights, you will become rich and have a beautiful wife. And of course, you will learn to shudder.'

'How wonderful!' said Anders.

'Many men have gone into the castle, but nobody has left.'

Hmm, thought Anders. *Maybe it is a very comfortable castle, and they did not want to leave.*

So he went and asked the King if he could go into the castle, and the King said, 'Yes, and you can bring three things with you.'

'I would like a fire, a lathe[9], and a knife.'

'A lathe? Are you sure?' said the King. 'Don't you want something more useful? Maybe an axe? What can a lathe do?'

'A lathe can do lots of things!' said Anders. 'You can make anything with a lathe and a knife. And I need the fire to keep warm, of course.'

An axe (pronunciation AKS). People use axes to cut wood.

So the King sent him to the castle with a fire, a lathe, and a knife. When night came, Anders made a fire and sat down on a chair.

'If only I could shudder!' he said. 'But I do not think I will learn it here.'

Then he heard a shout from a dark corner: 'Ow, meow[10]! It is so cold!'

'How stupid!' he said. 'If you are cold, come and sit by the fire.'

So two big black cats came and sat beside him. They looked at him with red eyes. They warmed themselves[11], and then said, 'Shall we play a game of cards?'

Anders did not think the cats were good. Black cats knew magic. So he said, 'Yes, let's. But first, show me your hands.'

So the cats did so, and he saw that
they had long claws.

'Oh, what long claws you have! I
will cut them for you.'

'How kind!' said the cats.

But Anders did not cut their
claws. He held the knife at them. 'I
know what you want. You want to
put those claws right in my eyes. No, thank you!'

*A paw (animal hand)
with long claws (they
can hurt you!)*

He threw them out of the window, into some water
below. But before he could sit down again, many black
cats and black dogs came out of the dark. They all had red
eyes, and they shouted and bit[12] him.

'Go away!' he shouted.

He took his knife and started cutting them. Some ran
away, but some stayed. He threw those ones out into the
water. But the animals came and came, and there were too
many. But then it turned midnight, and suddenly[13], all the
animals went away.

When Anders sat down again, he felt very tired. He
turned around and saw a bed in the corner.

'Perfect!' he said, and climbed into the bed.

But while he fell asleep[14], the bed started moving. It
walked around the castle like an insect.

'That's good,' he said. 'That will help me sleep. But go
faster.'

So the bed ran and ran, and Anders laughed. Finally,
the bed turned over and lay on top of him.

'That's no fun,' he said. He pushed the bed off him and slept by the fire.

In the morning, the King came and saw him on the floor. He thought the ghosts had killed him, but then the young man got up.

'What happened?' said the King.

'Good morning! Unfortunately, I did not learn to shudder last night, but lots of things happened.'

'You mean, you were not afraid?'

'Of course not! I slept very well.'

So the next night Anders went back into the castle and said again, 'If only I could shudder!'

A few hours later, there was a loud sound, and something fell from the ceiling. It was a man, but only half of him. There were no legs or feet.

'Hello!' cried Anders. 'The other half is not here! Where is the rest?'

So there was another sound, and the other half of the man fell down.

'I will make a fire for you,' he said.

When he turned around, the two halves were together, and a scary[15] man was sitting there.

'Excuse me, that chair is mine.'

Anders pushed him off the chair.

'Well then,' said the man. 'Let us play a game!'

From the ceiling fell some leg bones. On the ends of the bones were feet.

'Ah, we are going to go bowling!' said Anders. He put

the leg bones in a triangle. 'I love bowling. But where is the ball?'

Some skulls fell down as well.

'These are terrible balls! They are not round.'

So Anders took the skulls and put them on the lathe. He worked the skulls until they were round.

'There, now they will move very easily!'

A bone

They went bowling, and Anders did quite badly, but he had a lot of fun. But then, when it turned midnight, everything went away: the man, the skulls and the leg bones.

'Oh no! I didn't say goodbye.'

Bowling (pronunciation BO-ling)

He lay down and went to sleep.

The next morning, the King came and spoke to him again.

'How was it this time?'

'We went bowling.'

'But you did not learn how to shudder?'

A triangle (pronunciation TRAI-an-gul)

'No! It was great fun.'

On the third night, Anders sat on his chair and said, 'If only I could shudder!'

A few hours later, six tall men came in with a coffin[16]. They put the coffin in front of Anders.

'Ah, I think that's my cousin. He died only a few days ago.'

The men opened the coffin, but the man inside was too big to be Anders' cousin. But the stupid boy said, 'Cousin! You look so cold. Let me warm you.'

A skull

So Anders warmed his hand on the fire and held it to the man's face. But the body was still cold. So Anders carried him out of the coffin and put him by the fire. That also didn't help, so he carried him into the bed.

Finally, the body warmed up, and started to move.

'See, cousin? I have warmed you up!'

The dead man sat up and cried, 'Now I will eat you!'

'What?!' said Anders. 'That's how you thank me? Back to the coffin!'

So he threw his 'cousin' into the coffin and shut it. Then the six men came and carried the coffin away.

'I don't think I will ever learn to shudder!' said Anders.

'I can help you shudder…'

Anders turned around and saw an old man with a long white beard. He looked horrible.

'Soon you will shudder, because you will die!'

'I don't want to die!' said Anders, jumping out of the bed.

'Too bad! I'm going to kill you!'

'I don't think so,' said Anders. 'You don't look very strong.'

'Oh, I might not look strong, but I am,' said the old man. 'Let us have a competition. If you are stronger than me, I will let you go. Follow me...'

So they went through the castle. Finally, they arrived at a dark room, where there were some big stones and an axe.

Stones at the beach

The old man stood in front of the stone. He took the axe, and broke the stone in two with it.

'I can do better than that,' said Anders.

He went to another stone and took the axe. The old man stood and watched. Anders took the axe and broke the stone in two with it. Then he took the old man's beard, put it between the pieces of stone, and closed the stone on it.

'I can't move!' shouted the old man.

'Now I have you,' said Anders. 'Now you will die!'

He took a piece of stone and hit the old man with it until he cried, 'Please stop! I will show you where the gold is.'

So Anders let him go. The old man showed him through the castle, and they went to a room with three boxes of gold.

'One of these boxes is for the poor people, one is for the King, and the other is yours.'

But then, when it turned midnight, the old man went

away, and the light went away as well. Anders stood in the dark. He carefully found his way back to the fire and slept there.

The next morning, the King came and said, 'Did you learn how to shudder?'

'No, I did not. My dead cousin visited, and then a man with a beard came and showed me lots of gold, but nobody taught me to shudder.'

'Then you have done it. You stayed three nights in the castle, and you can get married to my daughter!'

'That is very good, but I still don't know how to shudder!'

So they brought out the gold and got married. Anders loved his wife, and was very happy, but every day he still said, 'If only I could shudder!'

Finally, his wife got angry. 'I will show him how to shudder!'

She went out to the river and took a bucket of cold water. At night, when Anders was asleep, his wife threw the bucket of water on him.

A bucket

Anders woke up and cried, 'Oh, what makes me shudder so much? What makes me shudder so, my wife? Ah! Now I know how to shudder!'

CINDERELLA

Once, there was a poor girl called Cinderella. Her mother died when she was young, and her father married[1] another woman. Cinderella's mother had been a lovely person, but Cinderella's stepmother[2] was a horrible person.

Cinderella's stepmother had two of her own daughters, Freta and Greta, and they were horrible as well. They made Cinderella do all the cooking and cleaning. Sometimes, their father said, 'Why don't you do that, Freta?' or 'I think you should do that, Greta,' but their mother always said, 'They are too beautiful to work!'

So Cinderella lived a sad life. She did all the work in the house, wore ugly[3] clothes and slept in the ashes[4] on the floor.

The only nice thing in Cinderella's life was the hazel tree in the garden. When her mother died, Cinderella planted[5] the tree in the garden, and it grew big and strong. Every night, Cinderella sat by the tree and cried. She was friends

Hazel trees make hazelnuts, that look like this.

with two little birds who lived in the tree, and when her stepsisters[6] were not looking, she played with the birds and sang songs.

One day, while Cinderella was cleaning the kitchen, her stepmother came in to say something. She was holding a letter.

'The King is having a ball[7] and everyone is invited,' she said.

'Yay, a ball!' said Freta and Greta.

'It will be three days long—'

'Yay, three days!' said Freta and Greta.

'—and there, the Prince[8] will choose his new wife.'

'Wow!' said Freta and Greta. 'We can get married to the Prince!'

Cinderella had never been to a ball before, but she had always wanted to go to one. And this was in the castle! Oh, what wonderful people would be there... She didn't know much about the Prince, but she wanted very much to go to the ball.

Over the next few days, the family started getting ready. Freta and Greta went into town to buy dresses. Every day, they asked Cinderella to make new bows, help them with their hair and change their dresses. Cinderella was very busy.

In a quiet moment, Cinderella went to her father and asked him if she could go to the ball.

'Yes, why not?' said her father.

Cinderella understood that she could go, and over the next few days she made some nice clothes for herself.

A bow (pronunciation BO)

But on the day of the ball, when Cinderella put on her dress and said she was ready to go, Freta and Greta laughed in her face.

'You want to go to the King's ball in *that*?! Did rats make that dress? I wouldn't wear it for a walk down the road.'

'But Father said—'

'Cinderella!' said her stepmother[9]. 'Do you really think you can go to the ball and make us look bad? You are not invited.'

'Don't worry, Cindy!' said Freta. 'You'll have something to do.'

'Here!' said Greta, giving her a bag filled with lentils. 'While we're gone, take out the bad lentils from the good ones.'

'If there is even *one* bad lentil in there when we come back, you'll have to start again!'

Almost crying, Cinderella watched her family climb into their carriage[10].

Different types of lentils

Oh, how awful[11] she felt! She threw all the lentils on the floor, but it was clear that the work would take at least until midnight, and she didn't have the energy[12] to do it.

She ran outside to her mother's tree and cried.

A minute later, she heard a bird singing by her ear, and looked up to see her two bird friends.

'What's wrong, Cinderella?' said one of them.

'You can talk?'

'Of course, of course. What's wrong, Cinderella?'

'Oh, it's only that... I was being stupid[13], really. I thought I could go to the King's ball, but of course I can't. I have to work on lentils in the ashes[14] while my sisters dance with wonderful people.'

'Show us these lentils, show us.'

So Cinderella took the birds inside and showed them the lentils.

'We can help, we can help! We will eat the bad ones and leave the good ones.'

'Oh, thank you. But I still cannot go to the ball!'

'Cinderella, Cinderella. Go out to the tree and shake[15] it.'

The birds started working, and Cinderella walked to the tree. She did not know why they were asking her to shake the tree, but she did as she was told. She shook the tree.

Out of the tree fell a large hazelnut. She opened the hazelnut, but inside there was not a nut[16], but a beautiful green dress! It was as beautiful as a fresh flower in spring.

Cinderella shook the tree again, and another nut fell. This time, there was not a dress inside, but a pair of lovely green shoes!

Her heart beating fast[17], she tried on the dress and shoes, and they fit her perfectly[18].

'Oh, Mother, thank you! But how can I go to the ball without a carriage[19]?'

She shook the tree again, and another nut fell. When she opened this one, a beautiful carriage with two horses and a servant[20] jumped out.

'Wow!' she said. 'I must go and get ready!'

Cinderella ran inside, washed herself, combed her hair and put on her clothes. She looked very different without the ashes and rags. She was beautiful.

The birds had finished with the lentils, and they flew around her happily, singing, 'To the ball, to the ball! But be careful, my dear. You must return before midnight, or all will be lost.'

Cinderella climbed into the carriage and went to the ball. She could hardly believe what was happening[21], and when she arrived at the castle, it was like a dream.

The building was beautiful and white, with marble stairs going to the entrance. Inside, it was filled with coloured lights, flowers from all around the world, and the most amazing guests with the most wonderful dresses.

Cinderella felt strange. This wasn't her place. Her dress was so simple, and she didn't know how to dance.

Marble, a type of stone

For a while, she just watched the dances, but soon, a man came and spoke to her.

'May I dance with you?'

He was the most handsome[22] man she had ever met, with hair as black as the night and eyes that were like stars.

'Yes, of course,' she said.

As the two danced around the room, everyone turned to look at her. People whispered[23] about them: '…beautiful girl…' '…who is she?…' '…and with the Prince[24]!'

Cinderella went as red as a tomato. She was dancing with the Prince!

The Prince smiled[25] at her, saying, 'You dance well, but this is your first time, isn't it?'

'How did you know?'

'It's clear, but don't worry. I like it.'

They danced more, and Cinderella saw her sisters in the corner. They looked very angry.

Cinderella smiled and enjoyed the dance. She felt free, but then she heard the clock strike eleven[26].

Then she remembered what the birds had said: return before midnight or all will be lost.

'I must go,' Cinderella said.

'Wait! Please stay for another dance.'

'Perhaps tomorrow night,' she said, before hurrying out the door.

She ran down the marble stairs into her carriage and went home.

Her heart beat fast[27] the whole way. She had never been so happy. She hoped her sisters had not seen her, but they were probably too stupid to know it was her.

When she arrived home, she quickly hid[28] the dress and shoes in the tree in the garden, changed into her normal clothes, changed her hair and put ashes on her face.

When the others returned a few hours later, Freta said, 'I hope Cinderella isn't sleeping! She should be working on those lentils!'

'The lentils aren't important,' said Greta. 'Who was that strange girl?'

Cinderella's family came in to see her, and she put on a sad face, so that they thought she had been working hard.

'Are you done already?' said Freta. 'We will give you something harder tomorrow night.'

'Come on, Sister,' said Greta. 'Let's go to bed.'

Cinderella smiled[29] and said, 'Good night!'

Her stepmother looked at her. 'Your hair looks different.'

'Oh?' Cinderella said. 'I tied it up while I worked.'

'Hrmm. Do not get any strange ideas about going to the ball tomorrow night or the night after that. You will stay here and work, understand?'

'Yes, Stepmother.'

This woman has her hair tied up in a ponytail.

'That's "Mother", you little...!' Cinderella thought she was going to hit her, so she put her hands on her head and shut her eyes. But her step-mother did not hit her. 'Good night, Cinderella.'

Clearly, she knew that something strange was happening.

Cinderella hardly slept that night[30], as she couldn't stop thinking about the ball. Oh, how handsome[31] the Prince had been!

The next day, her sisters gave her double the work[32] to do, but she worked with great energy[33], cleaning everything in no time.

'Why are you smiling so much, Cinderella?' said Greta. 'You're not going to the ball, you know!'

'Oh, I know! I just had a lovely dream.'

'Well, dream on[34]!' said Freta.

Part of Cinderella's happiness[35] came from hearing her sisters' conversation. Clearly, *everyone* had been talking about her dance with the Prince, and it was great to hear how bothered they were by it.

That night, Freta and Greta gave Cinderella a big bag of seeds[36].

'Take out the good seeds, lazy,' said Freta.

'And if we find even *one* bad one in there—'

'—I'll have to start again?'

'Yeah,' said Greta. 'Now shut your mouth and get to work!'

When the rest of the family had left, Cinderella's bird friends came in through the window.

'Oh, can you help me again tonight?'

'Of course, Cinderella, of course!' sang the birds. 'Go and shake[37] the tree, shake shake shake.'

So Cinderella ran out to the garden and shook the hazel tree again. She thought that the beautiful gifts might not fall down, but luckily, they did.

This time, she had a lovely blue dress, a pair of long gloves and dancing shoes. The shoes had a small heel[38], but Cinderella found she could walk fine in them, and she felt beautiful.

'Goodbye, little birds!' she said, running out to the carriage, 'and thank you again!'

'Remember, remember, return before midnight!'

This time, when Cinderella arrived everyone was waiting for her. She was even more[39] beautiful than the night before. Several men immediately came up to ask for a dance, but she said no to them all, as she was only interested in the Prince.

'I must say,' said the Prince as they started to dance, 'I was worried that you wouldn't return after your quick exit last night.'

'I am sorry. It was not polite of me.'

'Are you going to tell me why you left?'

'Don't worry, it was not because of you. I had... to do something.'

'Well, you are strange and beautiful! Will you tell me where you are from?'

'I live near here.'

'But I have never heard of you until this moment! Won't you tell me your name?'

'I am Bridget.'

That was Cinderella's true name, that her mother had chosen before she died. She was sure that her sisters and stepmother would not remember it.

'A beautiful name.'

This time, Cinderella danced until half past eleven, and then she looked at the clock.

'You have things to do tonight as well?'

'Yes, I am afraid, my Prince.'

'Well, will I at least see you again tomorrow night?'

'Of course.'

'Then I suppose you can go,' he said, smiling.

So Cinderella left again, running down the stairs and into the carriage before anyone else could talk to her.

Again, after arriving home she hid[40] the dress and shoes in the tree and made herself dirty. She made sure to change her hair as well.

'Oh, I'll kill that girl!' said Greta, as they walked through the door.

'Some were saying she is a foreign princess[41],' said Freta. 'Pah! I think she looked *horrible* in that dress.'

'Girls, go to bed,' said their mother. 'No talking through the night, understood?'

'Yes, mother!' they said.

They put their heads into the room where Cinderella was.

'We're going to give you *even more* work tomorrow,

Cindy!'

Then they climbed up the stairs, laughing and chatting about the handsome men they had met.

Cinderella was ready to sleep as well, but again, her stepmother came in to see her.

'Cinderella, dear child.'

Cinderella felt very cold. Her stepmother only called her 'dear child' when she wanted something.

'Yes, Mother?'

'What name did you have before?'

Cinderella quickly said, 'Britney.' She should have said something much more different to her real name, but the name just came out of her mouth.

'Oh?' said her stepmother. 'I was sure you were called Bridget.'

'Mother, I like my new name so much that I can hardly remember my old one!'

'Hmm,' said her stepmother. 'Well, you have worked well again tonight. Do the same tomorrow.'

Cinderella slept badly that night. She dreamt that she travelled to the ball for the final night, but as she danced, her stepmother came and took off her dress, showing her awful[42] rags[43].

'See? She is only a servant[44] girl!'

Cinderella woke up feeling sick.

That day, her sisters gave her lots of work, just like they had said. She had to water the flowers, cut the grass and give food to all the animals, as well as her normal cleaning. But as she worked, she heard her sisters talking.

'Oh, it is so sad that we only have one more night! The Prince still doesn't love me yet…'

'Don't worry, tonight is the night! We'll dance with *him* tonight, and it doesn't matter what that ugly[45] girl does. We're going to get married!'

'Not "we", stupid! We can't share a prince! He's going to be *mine*.'

'No! He'll be mine!'

They started fighting[46], but their words made Cinderella feel bad. She had enjoyed the ball so much that she had hardly thought about the future. As lovely as the Prince was, she would never be with him, because at midnight the magic would end and all her lovely clothes would go away. She would be a dirty, common servant girl, and he would be the handsome Prince.

But that night she still felt excited. It was only three nights, but they would be the most wonderful three nights of her life. She could not worry about the future. She just had to enjoy these nights while she could.

This time, her sisters gave her three big bags of peas[47] to sort through.

'You'll be working all night with these!' said the girls as they went out the door. 'If you don't see us again, it's because we're getting married to the Prince!'

Cinderella said goodbye, making herself not smile. Then, after she was sure they were gone, she opened the window and the birds flew in.

'I feel so bad giving you so much work…'

'Of course not, of course not! It's the last night, the last night. Go and enjoy yourself!'

So while the birds worked, she went and shook the tree. Tonight, the dress was the most beautiful one yet. It was a lovely long silver dress with a pair of high heels[48].

'I don't know if I can walk in these...'

But when she put them on, a strong energy filled her. She walked gracefully[49], like a foreign princess[50].

'Oh, how wonderful tonight will be!' she said to herself as she left.

When she arrived at the castle, everyone said, 'Wow!' She was even more beautiful than before, and everyone talked about how good she looked.

For a moment, the Prince looked sad.

'What's wrong, my Prince?'

'You are just so beautiful! I have never seen a dress or shoes quite like that... Come, let us dance!'

Cinderella danced with the Prince, and for the first time in many years she felt happy. She did not feel sad, and when she saw her sisters she did not even feel angry at them, but they certainly felt angry at her.

She enjoyed herself so much that she hardly felt the time pass[51]. She looked into the Prince's eyes the whole evening, as they had a conversation with their bodies.

But then the clock began to strike and Cinderella woke up from her dream. She looked up. It was twelve!

'I'm so sorry, my Prince, but I must leave.'

She moved out of his arms and ran through the hall. The clock struck behind her: two, three, four.

'Wait!' cried the Prince, taking her hand. 'You cannot leave. I must know—'

'You cannot!'

Five, six, seven.

Cinderella pulled herself free and ran outside.

Eight, nine.

But the Prince knew that she would try to escape[52], so he had covered the stairs with glue, and as she ran down them her shoes got stuck[53].

If you stand on glue, your feet will get stuck.

Ten, eleven.

She pulled her feet out of the shoes, leaving them stuck to the stairs, and ran into the night.

Twelve.

As she ran, her beautiful dress went away and the ugly rags came back. Her hair no longer looked pretty, and her old working shoes returned to her feet.

Her carriage was gone, so she ran all the way home.

She came through the door, threw herself on the floor and started crying. Oh, what a wonderful evening it had been, and how quickly it had passed! Now she had to return to her sad life, and she never even kissed the Prince.

Cinderella cried for several hours, and then dried her face. She didn't want her awful sisters and stepmother to see that she had been crying, so she put ashes on her face.

The rest of the family arrived with lots of noise, Freta and Greta laughing happily.

'Shh!' said their stepmother. 'You'll wake up the neighbours.'

'Oh, but Mother, it was such a wonderful night! And I *do* believe that man wants to marry[54] me.'

'That man does not have much money. I wanted you to make the Prince love you.'

'But that's not fair! That awful foreign princess stole him away the whole night. What could we do?'

'You could have done many things. Now off to bed.'

Luckily, Freta and Greta did not come in to talk to Cinderella, but her stepmother did.

'It was a lovely evening, wasn't it?'

'I wouldn't know, Mother, as I was working.'

Her stepmother smiled. 'And you worked very well. I thought that was enough work for two nights.'

'I did not stop once.'

'How lucky we are to have you, Bridget.'

Cinderella was surprised to hear her name, and her stepmother smiled.

'Remember, my dear, you will always live here. There are no happy endings[55] or handsome princes for you, understand?'

'Yes, Mother.'

'Good. Now get some sleep. From tomorrow, you will be helping Freta and Greta prepare for their weddings[56], as a man will certainly ask them to marry him.'

Cinderella lay down on the floor and waited for her

stepmother to leave. She felt sick. That was what the rest of her life would be: doing everything her horrible step-sisters wanted. When they got married, they would bring her with them and make her do all their work.

'Oh, Mother,' whispered[57] Cinderella. 'I need you.'

The next morning, the whole family was woken up by a loud noise.

'All listen! This is a message from the King!' cried a man.

Cinderella ran to the window. It was one of the King's men, standing on a carriage and reading from a piece of paper.

'The King is looking for the future wife of his son, the Prince. The woman who can wear these shoes and walk gracefully[58] will be the Prince's wife.'

The man held a pair of shoes—Cinderella's shoes from the night before! The magic had not taken them. Cinderella's heart beat fast. If she could try them on...

'Me first!' shouted Greta, running down the stairs.

'No, me!' cried Freta.

They started fighting[59], and fell on the floor.

'Girls!' shouted their mother. 'Get up immediately! If you are going to be the Prince's wife then you must be like a princess.'

Cinderella watched as they walked out to try on the shoes. But the King's servant looked at their feet and said, 'Sorry, ma'am[60], but their feet are too big to wear the shoes.'

'Well, can't they try?'

'We can't break the shoes before anyone else can try them.' He smiled. 'If your daughters' feet get smaller in the next few hours, they can try them on.'

The stepmother walked her daughters back inside and said, 'Freta, come with me into the kitchen.'

She took her into the room and shut the door behind her. Greta and Cinderella looked at each other, but Greta just said, 'What are you looking at, ugly?'

While her mother talked to Freta, Greta went to choose a dress 'for her wedding[61]'.

Cinderella went and put her ear to the kitchen door to hear what her stepmother and stepsister were saying.

'Mother, no!' said Freta.

'Stop crying, child! It will only hurt for a bit, but you will have a life of happiness afterwards. You can pay for new feet when you're queen.'

'Mother, I'm afraid!'

Freta started crying, and then she screamed[62].

'Be quiet!' shouted the stepmother.

Cinderella's eyes went wide. She couldn't be…?

After the screaming stopped, Cinderella ran and hid in the corner. A few moments later, the door opened and Cinderella's stepmother came out with Freta in her arms.

The girl was trying not to cry. Cinderella looked at her feet. They had bandages[63] on them, and blood was coming out.

The stepmother carried Freta outside to the King's servant.

'My daughter's feet were a bit swollen[64] because it is cold. The shoes will fit well[65] now.'

Cinderella watched through the window. The stepmother hid the girl's feet until the shoes were on, and then she pushed.

'Walk, dear,' she whispered.

But Freta just walked a bit and then fell.

'This is not the girl,' said the King's servant. 'She is not graceful.'

Freta started crying, pulled off the shoes and ran upstairs. For the first time in her life, Cinderella felt sorry for her[66].

'Who's next?' called the man.

The stepmother went inside and called Greta to the kitchen, but the girl didn't want to go.

'It will just hurt for a second, dear. Think of how rich we'll be afterwards!'

Cinderella covered her ears, but she still heard the awful screams. Then she went and watched through the window as Greta put on the magic shoes.

Greta tried to walk gracefully, but it was clear how much her feet hurt.

'Better,' said the man, 'but not graceful. She is not the girl who the Prince is looking for.'

Greta made herself smile and gave back the shoes.

'What's all this noise?' said Cinderella's father, coming down the stairs. 'I heard you screaming,' he said, looking at Greta.

'The Prince is looking for his wife, the strange

princess,' she said. 'The person who can walk in her shoes can marry him. But, but, but me and Freta couldn't do it!'

She started crying and fell into her father's arms.

'Don't cry, my child,' he said. 'Oh, Cinderella! Why don't you try?'

'No!' cried her stepmother. 'She's a dirty servant girl and nothing more.'

'Excuse me?' said her father. 'I told you to stop talking about her like that!'

'Is there another daughter at this house?' said the King's man, hearing the conversation.

'No!' said the stepmother.

'Yes!' said the father. 'She's here.'

He took Cinderella to the man.

'Don't be afraid, dear.'

'No, that's not fair!' said Greta.

'Everyone can try the shoes on,' said the King's man. 'Those were the Prince's words. Now, my dear, here are the shoes.'

The man gave Cinderella the shoes. Cinderella put them on.

They fit as perfectly as the night before, and immediately she felt the magic in her. She smiled, walked like a beautiful bird and curtseyed to the King's man.

'It's her! I didn't know it was you, because you have all those ashes and rags on you.'

'I am not a foreign princess, but I hope I am enough for the Prince.'

'More than enough!' said the Prince, and jumped out of the carriage.

He had been hiding there the whole time!

'You are a very beautiful girl, and you have had to live with such an ugly family.' He took her hand in his. 'I will not ask your father if I can marry you, because I want it so much that nothing could stop me. Bridget, will you be my wife?'

'Yes!' said the girl, and they kissed.

She had ashes on her, everyone was watching, her sisters and step-mother were crying, but it was the most magical[67] moment of her life. Everything else went away, and there was only her and the Prince.

They had their wedding a few weeks later. Her family were horrible, but she still invited them all. Her sisters came on crutches, because they could not

*A girl curtseying (pronunciation **KURT-see**)*

walk well. Her stepmother did not come.

Before the wedding, her father spoke to her.

'I'm so sorry, Bridget. I was a terrible father. I saw what was happening but I didn't say anything. And so that awful woman hurt you.

When you hurt your legs, you can use crutches to help you walk.

She was horrible to you and horrible to her own daughters.'

'What will you do, Father?'

'I am leaving her, and taking Freta and Greta with me.'

Cinderella's heart hurt. For so many years she thought she had lost her father, but now he was here again. She couldn't lose him again.

'Come live with us, in the castle.'

'I don't think the Prince will want us here now. No, we will go and live a simple life, and I will teach those girls to be good and kind. I want you to be happy, my dear.'

'But you'll come and visit, won't you?'

'Of course. I love you, Bridget. I'm just sorry I didn't show it before.'

So Cinderella went and got married. But she was not Cinderella anymore. She was Bridget, because she no longer had to clean up ashes and sleep on the floor. She was going to be queen, and she would never have to do such awful work again, or live with her horrible step-mother and stepsisters.

As Bridget and the Prince kissed, a pair of birds flew happily around them, and far away, in the garden of Bridget's house, a hazel tree moved in the wind.

AUTHOR'S NOTE

Thank you so much for reading *Easy Stories in English for Beginners*! I hope you enjoyed the book and found it helpful.

If you did enjoy the book, please think about writing a review[1]. Reviews will help other people find the books, and the more people read the books, the more I will be able to write!

If you want language learning advice, you can join my email newsletter. Every two weeks I will send you an email telling you the best ways to study English. If you join now, you can get my free PDF 'My Top 10 Language Learning Advice'.

Go to EasyStoriesInEnglish.com/Email to join! Or you can scan the QR code below:

You can find over a hundred stories, including audio and transcripts, at EasyStoriesInEnglish.com. Scan the QR code below to go there:

Or you can find the podcast on Spotify or Apple Podcasts!

If you *really* enjoyed the book and have something to say, you can email me at Ariel@EasyStoriesInEnglish.com. I love hearing from my readers and listeners, so don't be shy!

Now that you've read the beginner level of this book, why not try the pre-intermediate level? Take your English to the next level today!

VOCABULARY EXPLANATIONS AND REFERENCES

WHY YOU MUST READ

1. 100 People, *100 People: A World Portrait* <https://www.100people. org/statistics-100-people/> [accessed 4 January 2021].
2. Stephen Krashen, *The Power of Reading - Stephen Krashen* (5 April 2012) <https://www.youtube.com/watch?v=DSW7gmvDLag> [accessed 4 January 2021].
3. **Pleasure** (pronunciation **PLEZH-uh**) = fun
4. When you do an **experiment**, you try something new and see what happens. Scientists do experiments to learn more about the world.
5. **A crime** = something very bad that you shouldn't do, for example stealing food or killing someone
6. **Native speakers** = people who have spoken a language all their lives, for example English people are native speakers of English
7. When you do an **experiment**, you try something new and see what happens. Scientists do experiments to learn more about the world.
8. **The Fiji islands** (pronunciation **FEE-jee EYE-lands**) = a country made of islands east of Australia
9. **Silence** (pronunciation **SAI-lens**) = when there is no sound, when nobody is speaking
10. Warwick B. Elley, 'The Potential of Book Floods for Raising Literacy Levels', *International Review Of Education*, 46, (2000), 233-255.
11. **We learn them naturally** = we learn them without thinking, we learn them without trying to
12. **A podcast** = a show that you can listen to on your phone, like a radio programme
13. **Fairy tales** = famous stories like Cinderella and Hansel and Gretel, which people usually tell to children
14. Stephen Krashen, 'Aesthetic Reading: Efficient Enough', *Journal Of English Language Teaching*, 62.2, (2020), 3-4.

15. Jeff McQuillan, 'Where Do We Get Our Academic Vocabulary? Comparing the Efficiency of Direct Instruction and Free Voluntary Reading', *The Reading Matrix*, 19.1, (2019), 129-138.

16. **A novel** = a longer book with a story, for example *Harry Potter*

17. **Academic word lists** = lists of words that people need for university

18. Heather Rolls, Michael P.H. Rogers, 'Science-specific technical vocabulary in science fiction-fantasy texts: A case for 'language through literature", *English for Specific Purposes*, 48, (2017), 44-56.

19. **Science fiction** (pronunciation **SAI-ens FIK-shun**) = stories about science, for example *Star Wars* and *Star Trek*

20. **A novel** = a longer book with a story, for example *Harry Potter*

21. **A translation** is when you put something in a different language. For example, maybe you have read *Harry Potter* in German. This is a translation, because the book was in English first.

22. **Latin American** = people from Latin America, countries like Peru, Argentina, Mexico and so on

23. **An author** (pronunciation **AWW-thuh**) = someone who writes books

24. **A podcast** = a show that you can listen to on your phone, like a radio programme

25. **Native speakers** = people who have spoken a language all their lives, for example English people are native speakers of English

26. **I learned them naturally** = I learned them without thinking, I learned them without trying to

27. Stephen Krashen, 'Self-Selected Fiction: The Path to Academic Success?', *CATESOL Newsletter*, (2020), 1-2.

28. **An expert** = someone who knows a lot about something, a professor

29. **A detective story** = a story where someone has died and someone else (the detective) wants to find out who killed them

30. **Romance stories** = stories about love

31. Quote adapted from:
      Stephen Krashen, 'The Case for Narrow Reading', *Language Magazine*, 3.5, (2004), 17-19.

32. Marcella Hu, Paul Nation, 'Unknown Vocabulary Density and Reading Comprehension', *Reading In A Foreign Language*, 13.1, (2000), 403-430.

33. **A text** = a piece of writing, a book, an article and so on

34. Here is the text with no nonsense words:

Jerry jumped out of bed and opened the curtains. He sang to himself as he made breakfast. He made coffee and put butter on his toast. Someone called his phone, and he picked it up. He was very surprised by who was calling, so his food fell on the floor.

35. The idea for this came from:

    Marcos Benevides, *Extensive Reading: How easy is easy?* (2015) <https://www.slideshare.net/MarcosBenevides/how-easy-is-easy> [accessed 4 January 2021].

36. **Pleasure** (pronunciation **PLEZH-uh**) = fun

37. **To follow the story** = to understand what is happening in the story

38. **Audio** (pronunciation **AWW-dee-oh**) = sound

39. **An episode** = a part of a programme. Usually there is a new episode every week.

THE NORTH WIND AND THE SUN

1. A **human** (pronunciation **HYOO-man**) is a person. A human is not an animal, insect or alien. Humans live on the planet Earth. I am a human, and you are a human. Another name for human is 'homo sapiens'.

2. When you want to hurt someone, you might **fight** (pronunciation **FITE**, past tense **fought**, past participle **fought**) them. You might fight them with a knife, a gun, or you can just use your hands. You might fight them with words—an argument. Children sometimes throw food at each other—a food fight. A war is like a big fight.

3. **Weak** (pronunciation **WEEK**) = not strong

4. **They will simply hurt you** = they will just hurt you, they will only hurt you

5. When you **smile**, you move the sides of your mouth up. Like this: :)

    It is like a laugh, but smaller. You want to show that you are happy. If you like someone, you smile at them.

6. When the wind makes a sound, it **blows** (pronunciation **BLO**, past tense **blew**, past participle **blown**). It goes *whoosh whoosh*. If the wind is blowing very strongly, it can be hard to walk around.

7. **Suddenly** = very quickly

STRANGE FRIENDS

1. **Fat** is something we all have in our body. It is under the skin. If you eat a lot of food, you will have lots of fat, but if you eat less food, you will have less fat. We take fat out of animals to use for various things. For example, people often use pig fat when cooking.

2. In Christianity, when a child is born, the parents choose a **godmother** and a **godfather**. They say, 'I will help look after the child,' and they often give them presents and so on. The godmother and godfather are chosen at an event called a christening.

3. In Christianity, when a child is born, there is an event called a **christening** (pronunciation **KRIH-suh-ning**). You put water on the baby's head, and you give the baby a name. Two friends of the parents become the godmother and godfather. They say, 'I will help look after the child,' and they often give them presents and so on.

4. When you **lie**, you say something that isn't true. For example, if I tell you, 'Hi, I'm Queen Elizabeth,' that's a lie, because it's not true. I am not Queen Elizabeth. Children often lie when they don't want their parents to get angry at them. Sometimes, people lie because it is very hard to say the truth.

5. In your mouth, you have a big pink thing called a **tongue** (pronunciation **TUNG**). When you put your tongue on something, you **lick** it. For example, you lick ice creams to eat them. You lick an envelope to close it. When you **lick your lips**, the bit around your mouth, it is because you are hungry and you are thinking about food.

6. A **godchild** = the child who a godmother and godfather look after

7. '**Good things come in threes**' is a phrase. We say it when we have three good things together.

8. A **paw** is a hand, but an animal's hand. Animals don't have fingers like us, so they have paws. Cat paws are really cute.

9. In your mouth, you have a big pink thing called a **tongue** (pronunciation **TUNG**). When you put your tongue on something, you **lick** it. For example, you lick ice creams to eat them. You lick an envelope to close it. When you **lick your lips**, the bit around your mouth, it is because you are hungry and you are thinking about food.

10. In Christianity, when a child is born, there is an event called a **christening** (pronunciation **KRIH-suh-ning**). You put water on the baby's head, and you give the baby a name. Two friends of the

parents become the godmother and godfather. They say, 'I will help look after the child,' and they often give them presents and so on.

THE VERY HUNGRY DRAGON

1. **Vitamins** are things that you find in food. They are very important for our health. For example, we get vitamin C from oranges. Vitamin C is important when you are ill, so when you are ill, people often say, 'Drink lots of orange juice.' Another important vitamin is vitamin D, which we get from the sun.

2. **Taste** is how food feels in your mouth. Basically, it is whether it is good food or not. For example, I think McDonald's tastes good, but some people think it tastes bad. I think dark chocolate tastes better than milk chocolate, but you might think the opposite. If something 'tastes of nothing', then it has no taste.

3. When you **spit** (past tense **spat**), you throw water or food out of your mouth. In the UK, people don't spit outside, but in the past, people used to eat tobacco and spit it out. If you eat some very bad food, you might spit it out.

4. You **smell** (past tense **smelt** or **smelled**) with your nose. Usually, you smell without thinking. If food smells very bad, you shouldn't eat it. If a person smells very bad, you shouldn't kiss them!

5. **Emerald** (pronunciation **EM-uh-ruld**) = a type of green jewel

6. **Ignore** is when you don't look at something or don't listen to something. For example, you might see someone you know outside, but you don't like them. You ignore them. You think, 'I don't see you!' but you really do see them. It is very bad to ignore someone when they are talking to you!

7. **Eugh** (pronunciation **ERKH**) = a sound you make when you think something is disgusting

8. You **smell** (past tense **smelt** or **smelled**) with your nose. Usually, you smell without thinking. If food smells very bad, you shouldn't eat it. If a person smells very bad, you shouldn't kiss them!

9. A **merchant** is a person who sells things. In the past, merchants travelled to different countries and sold things there. Now, we have trucks and aeroplanes to carry things and sell them. A **merchant road** is a road that merchants travel on.

10. **Eating all of the jewels in one go** = she ate all the jewels at the same time, she ate them very quickly

11. **Reputation** (pronunciation **reh-pyoo-TAY-shun**) is what people think of you. If you have a good reputation, people think you are good, and if you have a bad reputation, people think you are bad. Reputation is very important for famous people and politicians.

12. **Putting herself in danger** = doing dangerous things

13. **Her mother had different ideas** = her mother did not think the same, her mother wanted her to do something else

14. **Ignore** is when you don't look at something or don't listen to something. For example, you might see someone you know outside, but you don't like them. You ignore them. You think, 'I don't see you!' but you really do see them. It is very bad to ignore someone when they are talking to you!

15. A **freezer** is a piece of furniture in the kitchen. Freezers make things very cold, colder than a fridge. If you put water in a freezer, it turns into ice. You also put ice cream in a freezer. Many fridges have freezers in them.

16. **To search** (pronunciation **SERCH**) = to look for something in a place, to go through a place and look for something

17. When you know something that other people don't know, you have a **secret** (pronunciation **SEE-kret**). For example, maybe you saw that your sister didn't do her homework, but she told your mother that she did her homework. She has a secret, that she didn't actually do her homework, and you know her secret. Usually, secrets are more important than that. For example, someone might steal something and keep it a secret from everyone.

18. **Taste** is how food feels in your mouth. Basically, it is whether it is good food or not. For example, I think McDonald's tastes good, but some people think it tastes bad. I think dark chocolate tastes better than milk chocolate, but you might think the opposite. If something 'tastes of nothing', then it has no taste.

19. When you see a friend or someone from your family, you might **hug** them. You put your arms around them and hold them very close. In some countries, people hug more than in others. In Spain, people hug a lot, and kiss each others' cheeks. In Japan, people don't hug very often.

20. **I should have never made you change** = it was bad for me to make you change, you are good as you are

21. **From now on** = starting from now, after this time

DOGGO AND KITTY DO THEIR LAUNDRY

1. **Thick hair** = when there is lots of hair close together
2. **Messy** = dirty, not tidy
3. **Laundry** (pronunciation **LAWN-dree**) = when you wash your clothes, the clothes that need washing
4. **Tasty** (pronunciation **TAY-stee**) = food that is good, food that has a good flavour
5. **Eugh** (pronunciation **ERKH**) = a sound you make when you think something is disgusting
6. When you have something in your throat, you **cough** (pronunciation **KOFF**). You push the air out of your body and make a loud sound. People cough a lot when they are ill. If you are coughing too much, you can have cough medicine to help your throat.
7. **Laundry** (pronunciation **LAWN-dree**) = when you wash your clothes, the clothes that need washing
8. When you move your hand backwards and forwards on something, you **rub** it. For example, when you make a mistake when writing, you use a rubber, or an eraser, to rub out the mistake. When you shower, you rub soap on your body.
9. When you put lots of things together, you make a **pile**. For example, if you have lots of clothes in your room, and you are very lazy, you might throw them on the floor. Over time, you will throw more and more clothes, and they will make a pile—like a little mountain of clothes.
10. When you hold something very tight in your hands, you **squeeze** it. For example, when you make some drinks, you might squeeze a lemon into the drink. When you wash your hair, you squeeze the hair to get the water out. If you squeeze your arm very hard, it will go red.
11. **The sun shone** (pronunciation **SHON**, from **shine**) = the sun made light, gave light
12. **The sun shone** (pronunciation **SHON**, from **shine**) = the sun made light, gave light

DOGGO AND KITTY TEAR THEIR
TROUSERS

1. **Laundry** (pronunciation **LAWN-dree)** = when you wash your clothes, the clothes that need washing
2. **Shining so bright** = shining so strongly, shining so much
3. **Parasol** (pronunciation **PAH-ruh-sol)** = an umbrella for the sun
4. **Even** = both ears are up, or both ears are down
5. **Hide-and-seek** is a game that children play. One child closes their eyes and counts: one, two, three, four... The other children run and **hide** somewhere (past tense **hid**, past participle **hidden**). They go somewhere where you can't see them. Then the first child has to find them.
6. **Bush** = a small tree, a short green plant
7. **Uneven** = not even
8. When you **tear** something (past tense **tore**, past participle **torn**), you pull it so that it breaks. If you pull your clothes, they can tear. You can tear a piece of paper easily. You can also tear hair out of your head, but this hurts a lot.
9. **Bush** = a small tree, a short green plant
10. **Continued on their way** = they continued walking, they kept walking, they walked more
11. **To mend** = to fix, to repair
12. When you **tear** something (past tense **tore**, past participle **torn**), you pull it so that it breaks. If you pull your clothes, they can tear. You can tear a piece of paper easily. You can also tear hair out of your head, but this hurts a lot.
13. **A hole** = a space, an empty place, a part with no fabric
14. **Violence** = shouting, hurting people, hitting people, breaking things
15. **A seamstress** (pronunciation **SEEM-struss)** = a woman who makes and repairs clothes
16. **To mend** = to fix, to repair
17. When you **hide** (past tense **hid**, past participle **hidden**), you make it so people can't see you. Maybe you don't want your teacher to see you, because you forgot to do the homework, so you hide behind a door.
18. **A hole** = a space, an empty place
19. **Paws** = animal hands

20. **Violence** = shouting, hurting people, hitting people, breaking things

DOGGO AND KITTY BAKE A CAKE

1. **To celebrate** (pronunciation **SEH-luh-brayt**) = to have a party, to enjoy a holiday
2. **Ingredients** (pronunciation **in-GREE-dee-unts**) = food you need to cook something, for example rice, chicken, tomato sauce and salt
3. You find lots of **sand** at the beach. It is very small and brown and you walk over it. You can use sand to make sand castles.
4. When you have water in a bottle, but you want to have it in a glass, you **pour** (pronunciation **PAW**) it. When you pour beer, you have to be careful so that the beer does not all turn into white stuff called foam, because the foam then goes away and you have less beer to drink.
5. You smell (past tense **smelled** or **smelt**) with your nose. Usually, you smell without thinking. If food smells very bad, you shouldn't eat it. If a person smells very bad, you shouldn't kiss them!
6. When you **pretend**, you do something but you don't *really* do it. For example, if you pretend to eat, you don't actually put the food in your mouth. If you pretend to drink, you don't actually put the drink in your mouth. If you pretend to know something, you say, 'Oh yes, I know that!' but really you don't.
7. **Delicious** (pronunciation **dih-LIH-shus**) = very good food
8. **Five times as good** = 5x as good ('five times five' = 5 x 5)
9. When you have water in a bottle, but you want to have it in a glass, you **pour** (pronunciation **PAW**) it. When you pour beer, you have to be careful so that the beer does not all turn into white stuff called foam, because the foam then goes away and you have less beer to drink.
10. **Greasy** (pronunciation **GREE-see**) = has a lot of oil in it, has a lot of fat in it, like burgers, chips, bacon and so on
11. **To cool** = to get cold
12. When a child is very bad, they are **naughty** (pronunciation **NAW-tee**). For example, naughty children hit other children, steal things and don't do their homework. They are not nice.

13. You smell (past tense **smelled** or **smelt**) with your nose. Usually, you smell without thinking. If food smells very bad, you shouldn't eat it. If a person smells very bad, you shouldn't kiss them!

14. **To water** = to make water, to give out water

15. You find **mud** outside in the garden. It is brown and has water in it. If you get mud on your clothes, you have to wash them. Pigs love to play in the mud.

16. **A pie** = a dessert, like a cake

SLEEPING BEAUTY

1. **Her land** = her country, her home

2. **Wings** = fairies use their wings to fly

3. **To attack** (pronunciation **uh-TAK**) = to try to hurt someone, to try to kill someone

4. **Tear** (pronunciation **TEER**) = water that comes out of your eyes when you cry

5. **Beauty** (pronunciation **BYOO-tee**) = being beautiful

6. When you **smile**, you move the sides of your mouth up. Like this: :)
    It is like a laugh, but smaller. You want to show that you are happy. If you like someone, you smile at them.

7. **Gladiator** (pronunciation **GLAH-dee-ay-tuh**) = a man who fights other men in a stadium as a sport

8. **Head of the guards** (pronunciation **GAADZ**) = the most important guard, the guard who told the other guards what to do

9. **Handsome** (pronunciation **HAN-sum**) = pretty, beautiful (for a man)

10. **To shake your head** (past tense **shook**, past participle **shaken**) = to move your head left and right, to say 'no' with your head

11. **Walked towards her** = walked to her, walked closer to her

12. When something very bad happens to you, you **suffer**. You feel very bad. You might suffer because your body hurts a lot, or because people are not nice to you.

13. **To fall asleep** (past tense **fell**, past participle **fallen**) = to start sleeping, to go to sleep

14. **A musician** (pronunciation **myoo-ZIH-shun**) = a person who plays music

15. When you move something very quickly, you **shake** it (past tense **shook**, past participle **shaken**). For example, if your friend is asleep,

you can shake them to wake them up. If you shake a can of Coca Cola, when you open it the drink will go everywhere. If you hurt your hand, you might shake it.

16. **Delicious** (pronunciation **dih-LIH-shus**) = very good food

17. **Tear** (pronunciation **TEER**) = water that comes out of your eyes when you cry

18. **To break something up** (past tense **broke**, past participle **broken**) = to break something into two pieces, to separate something

19. **Earth** (pronunciation **ERTH**) is the brown thing we find outside. Trees and flowers live in the earth. Grass grows on the earth.

ONE-EYED, TWO-EYED, THREE-EYED

1. **To work hard** = to work a lot

2. **A fringe** (British; pronunciation **FRINJ**) = hair that goes over your head, hair that goes over your eyes

3. **To marry someone** = to get married to someone, to become a husband or wife to someone

4. **Suddenly** = very quickly

5. **To work hard** = to work a lot

6. **Skin** is the outside part of the body. Humans can have dark skin or light skin. Some people have lots of hair on their skin, but others don't. If your skin is hard or rough, you can use cream to make it nice and smooth.

7. **Goats** (pronunciation **GOTE**) are a short, white animal that go 'Meeeh!' and can climb mountains easily. Goats can be used to make milk, cheese and meat.

8. **Suddenly** = very quickly

9. **Asleep** = sleeping

10. **Awake** = not asleep, not sleeping

11. **Continued to sing** = kept singing, sang more, did not stop singing

12. Your **voice** is the thing you use to speak. You can use a loud voice or a quiet voice, a high voice or a low voice. Everyone's voice is different.

13. **Continued to sing** = kept singing, sang more, did not stop singing

14. Your **voice** is the thing you use to speak. You can use a loud voice or a quiet voice, a high voice or a low voice. Everyone's voice is different.

15. **A fringe** (British; pronunciation **FRINJ**) = hair that goes over your head, hair that goes over your eyes
16. When you want to put something underground, you need to **dig** (past tense **dug**). You dig using a wide tool called a shovel, but you can also dig with your hands. When you dig, you make a **hole**, an empty space in the ground. Dogs often dig with their hands and put bones in the hole. In crime films, people often dig holes and put dead bodies in them.
17. **To pick apples** = to pull apples off a tree, to take apples from a tree
18. **Could not pick a single apple** = could not pick any apples

THE BOY WHO KNEW NO FEAR

1. **Stupid** (pronunciation **STYOO-pid**) = not intelligent, not clever
2. When you **shudder**, you shake. You move a bit because you are scared or cold. The hairs on your arms stand up. If you don't want to show that you are scared, you can try and stop yourself from shuddering. But sometimes you are so scared that you cannot stop yourself.
3. Something **scary** makes you feel afraid, makes you feel frightened. It is something bad and dangerous. For example, lions are scary, because lions can kill you easily. Many people think clowns are scary. Some people like watching scary films.
4. **Stupid** (pronunciation **STYOO-pid**) = not intelligent, not clever
5. **If only I could shudder!** = I really want to shudder, I wish I could shudder
6. **You must be cold** = I think you are cold
7. **To burn** = when fire eats something
8. **If only I could shudder!** = I really want to shudder, I wish I could shudder
9. A **lathe** (pronunciation **LAYTH**) is a thing that turns something around. So when you make pottery, you use a lathe. Pottery is mugs, pots and so on. You put the clay, the thing you use to make pottery, on the lathe, and it turns it around. Then you use your hands to make the pottery. You can also use lathes to make things out of wood, for example.
10. **Meow** (pronunciation **mee-AU**) = the sound a cat makes
11. **They warmed themselves** = they made themselves warm

12. **Bite** (past tense **bit**, past participle **bitten**) is when you put your teeth in something and hurt it. When you eat food, you bite it first. Dogs might bite someone if they are dangerous. Insects also bite people and they can be very annoying.

13. **Suddenly** = very quickly

14. **To fall asleep** (past tense **fell**, past participle **fallen**) = to start sleeping, to go to sleep

15. Something **scary** makes you feel afraid, makes you feel frightened. It is something bad and dangerous. For example, lions are scary, because lions can kill you easily. Many people think clowns are scary. Some people like watching scary films.

16. **A coffin** = a box you go in when you die

CINDERELLA

1. **To marry someone** = to get married to someone, to become a husband or wife to someone

2. If your mother dies and your father gets married again, his new wife will be your **stepmother**. In fairy tales, stepmothers are usually horrible people.

3. **Ugly** = not pretty, not beautiful

4. **Ashes** are what you get when you burn something. When you burn something with fire, it goes black, and then it turns into thin grey things called ashes. When you burn wood, you get ashes. Also, when someone dies, you burn their body, cremate it, and then you can keep their ashes.

5. **To plant a tree** = to put a tree in the ground so that it grows

6. If your mother dies and your father gets married again, his new wife will be your stepmother. If your stepmother has her own daughters, they will be your **stepsisters**.

7. **A ball** = a big party with lots of dancing

8. **A prince** = the son of a king

9. If your mother dies and your father gets married again, his new wife will be your **stepmother**. In fairy tales, stepmothers are usually horrible people.

10. A **carriage** (pronunciation **KAH-rij**) is a vehicle, a way of getting around, like a car. Usually, carriages are pulled by horses, and someone sits on top of the carriage and tells the horses to move. Before cars existed, carriages were the main way of travelling.

11. **Awful** = very bad

12. We use **energy** (pronunciation **EN-er-jee**) to do things every day. We have to eat food and sleep to have more energy. If you are very tired, you have no energy. Sports use a lot of energy.

13. **Stupid** (pronunciation **STYOO-pid**) = not intelligent, not clever

14. **Ashes** are what you get when you burn something. When you burn something with fire, it goes black, and then it turns into thin grey things called ashes. When you burn wood, you get ashes. Also, when someone dies, you burn their body, cremate it, and then you can keep their ashes.

15. **To shake something** = to move something quickly

16. **A nut** = a kind of brown food that grows on trees

17. **Her heart was beating fast** = her heart was going BADUM BADUM very quickly, her heart was working quickly

18. **They fit her perfectly** = they were the right size for her

19. A **carriage** (pronunciation **KAH-rij**) is a vehicle, a way of getting around, like a car. Usually, carriages are pulled by horses, and someone sits on top of the carriage and tells the horses to move. Before cars existed, carriages were the main way of travelling.

20. A **servant** is a person who lives in your house and helps you do things. For example, servants do cleaning, cooking and washing. Servants were very common in the past. The British TV show *Downton Abbey* is about servants.

21. **She could hardly believe it** = it was hard to believe it

22. **Handsome** (pronunciation **HAN-sum**) = pretty, beautiful (for a man)

23. **To whisper** = to talk very quietly, to talk not loudly, when you don't want other people to hear

24. **A prince** = the son of a king

25. When you **smile**, you move the sides of your mouth up. Like this: :)
    It is like a laugh, but smaller. You want to show that you are happy. If you like someone, you smile at them.

26. **The clock strikes eleven** = it is eleven o'clock and the clock makes a loud sound (DONG DONG) eleven times

27. **Her heart beat fast** = her heart was going BADUM BADUM very quickly, her heart was working quickly

28. When you **hide** something (past tense **hid**, past participle **hidden**), you make it so someone can't see it. For example, maybe you are eating chocolate, but you don't want other people to see it, because

then they will want to eat the chocolate. So you hide the chocolate in the cupboard so that they won't see it.

29. When you **smile**, you move the sides of your mouth up. Like this: :)

    It is like a laugh, but smaller. You want to show that you are happy. If you like someone, you smile at them.

30. **Hardly slept that night** = almost didn't sleep that night

31. **Handsome** (pronunciation **HAN-sum**) = pretty, beautiful (for a man)

32. **Double the work** = 2x the work, twice as much work

33. We use **energy** (pronunciation **EN-er-jee**) to do things every day. We have to eat food and sleep to have more energy. If you are very tired, you have no energy. Sports use a lot of energy.

34. **Dream on** = keep dreaming, dream more

35. **Happiness** = being happy

36. When you want to grow a plant, you first need a **seed**. A seed is a small, brown thing that you put in the ground. You put water on a seed, and the sun shines on it, and slowly it grows into a plant. You can also eat seeds, and they're very good for you. Common types of seeds are sunflower seeds, pumpkin seeds and sesame seeds.

37. **To shake something** = to move something quickly

38. **The heel** = the back part of the shoe that holds it up, the tall part of a shoe at the back

39. **Even more beautiful** = much more beautiful

40. When you **hide** something (past tense **hid**, past participle **hidden**), you make it so someone can't see it. For example, maybe you are eating chocolate, but you don't want other people to see it, because then they will want to eat the chocolate. So you hide the chocolate in the cupboard so that they won't see it.

41. **A princess** = the daughter of a king

42. **Awful** = very bad

43. **Rags** = dirty old clothes

44. A **servant** is a person who lives in your house and helps you do things. For example, servants do cleaning, cooking and washing. Servants were very common in the past. The British TV show *Downton Abbey* is about servants.

45. **Ugly** = not pretty, not beautiful

46. When you want to hurt someone, you might **fight** them (pronunciation **FITE**; past tense **fought**). You might fight them with a knife, a gun, or you can just use your hands. You might fight them with

words—an argument. Children sometimes throw food at each other —a food fight. A war is like a big fight.

47. **Peas** (pronunciation **PEEZ**) = small round green vegetables

48. **High heels** = shoes with a high heel, the back part of the shoe that holds it up, the tall part of a shoe at the back

49. **Gracefully** = moving very easily, walking in a beautiful way

50. **A princess** = the daughter of a king

51. When **time passes**, it goes by. For example, if it is 3pm, and five minutes pass, then it will be 3:05pm.

52. When you are in prison, or someone has caught you, you will want to **escape**, run away. There are many films about prisoners who want to escape, for example *Shawshank Redemption*. But it's not always that dramatic. Maybe you are at a family dinner and your parents start asking when you are going to get married and have children. You might escape to the toilet!

53. When something **gets stuck**, it stops and cannot move anymore. For example, if you are driving and there is a lot of mud, dirt, your car might get stuck, and then you can't drive anymore. Or maybe you are doing really difficult maths homework and you can't solve a problem. You get stuck, and can't move on.

54. **To marry someone** = to get married to someone, to become a husband or wife to someone

55. **A happy ending** = when a story ends happily, when everything is good for the people in a story

56. **A wedding** = a big party when two people get married

57. **To whisper** = to talk very quietly, to talk not loudly, when you don't want other people to hear

58. **Gracefully** = moving very easily, walking in a beautiful way

59. When you want to hurt someone, you might **fight** them (pronunciation **FITE**; past tense **fought**). You might fight them with a knife, a gun, or you can just use your hands. You might fight them with words—an argument. Children sometimes throw food at each other —a food fight. A war is like a big fight.

60. **Ma'am** (pronunciation **MAAM**) = a polite way to call a woman

61. **A wedding** = a big party when two people get married

62. **Scream** is when you go 'AAAAAAHHHHH!'. It is a very loud sound. People scream when they are scared or very angry.

63. **Bandages** (pronunciation **BAN-dij**) are soft, white things that you put on when you are hurt. If you cut your leg very badly, you will

need to put a bandage around it. Usually, doctors put bandages on people.

64. **Swollen** (pronunciation **SWO-lun**; present tense **swell**) = when part of your body gets bigger because you are ill

65. **Fit well** = they will be the right size

66. **To feel sorry for someone** = when someone is sad and you feel bad about it

67. **Magical** = magic, having magic

AUTHOR'S NOTE

1. **A review** is when you write about a book you read, saying what you liked and didn't like, and give it a rating (1-5 stars).

IMAGE ATTRIBUTIONS

DOGGO AND KITTY BAKE A CAKE

Bag of flour by DinosoftLabs is from Flaticon.com.

'Springform Pan with the walls loosened from the finished product.' by RibbonsOfIndecision is licensed under CC BY-SA 3.0.

'Sous les galets, la plage' by Daplaza is licensed under CC BY-SA 3.0; cropped.

'Fancy raw mixed nuts macro' by Sage Ross is licensed under CC BY-SA 3.0.

'Cucina dotata di timer cottura, quattro fornelli e forno a gas' by Antonio Mette is licensed under CC BY-SA 4.0.

'Bacon in a pan' by Joy is licensed under CC BY 2.0.

'Kurkkuja' by Muu-karhu is licensed under CC BY-SA 3.0.

Bone by Freepik is from Flaticon.com.

SLEEPING BEAUTY

Fairy by Flat Icons is from Flaticon.com.

'Cloak' by David Ring is in the public domain.

One Man Walking by Freepik is from Flaticon.com.

ONE-EYED, TWO-EYED, THREE-EYED

'One whole, deli dill pickle' by National Cancer Institute is in the public domain.

THE BOY WHO KNEW NO FEAR

CINDERELLA

'Hazelnuts' by Fir0002 is licensed under CC BY-SA 3.0.

Bow by Freepik is from Flaticon.com.

'Lens culinaris seeds' by Rainer Zenz is in the public domain.

'MarmiForoTraianoRoma' by MM is in the public domain.

Female head with ponytail by Freepik is from Flaticon.com.

'AdhesivesForHouseUse004' by Babi Hijau is in the public domain.

'Curtsy (PSF)' by Pearson Scott Foreman is in the public domain.

'Axillary Crutches' by Jessica Fisher is licensed under CC BY-SA 4.0.

Made in United States
North Haven, CT
14 November 2023

44007350R00082